目次

Level 3　Test 1—Test 40

嗨！你今天練習了嗎？
完成一回習題後，你可以在該回次的○打勾並在 100 填寫成績。
一起檢核英文實力吧！

Level 4 Test 1—Test 40

Level 5–1 Test 1—Test 20

Level 3 Test 1

Class: ________ No.: ________ Name: ________ Score: ________

I. 文意字彙 (40%)

________ 1. I have an upset s____h now because I ate too much yesterday.

________ 2. Apart from verbal language, people also use body language to c____e with each other.

________ 3. Everyone in the office was i____med that the meeting was canceled.

________ 4. My wallet was here a minute ago, but now it has v____hed into thin air.

________ 5. I am grateful that all my teachers teach me with great p____e.

II. 字彙配合 (請忽略大小寫) (40%)

(A) sticky (B) temporary (C) award (D) van (E) poverty

____ 1. Dora's house was damaged by the typhoon, so she is living in a(n) ____ shelter.

____ 2. We have to rent a(n) ____ because there are seven of us traveling together.

____ 3. The old man has lived in ____ since he lost his vision.

____ 4. The swimmer finally beat other competitors and won the ____.

____ 5. Dan had difficulty removing the price tags because they were very ____.

III. 選擇題 (20%)

____ 1. In old time, people lived in ____ instead of houses.
(A) caves (B) awards (C) knits (D) roughs

____ 2. Tim has ____ his manager that the project is a good investment.
(A) enabled (B) awarded (C) persuaded (D) knitted

____ 3. Sammy ____ butter with olive oil in cooking for the sake of health.
(A) dines (B) replaces (C) allows (D) convinces

____ 4. The poor grades Ed got in TOEFL burst his ____ of studying abroad.
(A) poverty (B) bubble (C) ownership (D) replacement

____ 5. Hannah ran the ____ of losing her life to save the drowning boy.
(A) passage (B) county (C) bubble (D) risk

Level 3 Test 2

Class: ________ No.: ________ Name: ________ Score: ________

I. 文意字彙 (40%)

________ 1. I was soaking wet because the rain came down in b______ts.

________ 2. This YouTube video teaches you how to deal with all kinds of dangerous s______ns.

________ 3. Tom's suggestion was not p______l, so it was not accepted.

________ 4. A genius is someone who is much more i______t than other people.

________ 5. The two countries are c______ted to each other by a bridge.

II. 字彙配合 (請忽略大小寫) (40%)

(A) strategy (B) threat (C) tourist (D) vision (E) passion

_____ 1. Acid rain is a _____ to the natural environment.

_____ 2. The London Eye is an example of London's _____ attraction.

_____ 3. Our company's business _____ to survive the economic depression is to reduce unnecessary expenses.

_____ 4. Peter wishes he had good _____ and didn't have to wear glasses.

_____ 5. Jeremy and his girlfriend share a _____ for classical music.

III. 選擇題 (20%)

_____ 1. Daisy kissed her son on the _____ and said "Good morning."
(A) stool (B) pile (C) bamboo (D) cheek

_____ 2. Time cannot _____ the old woman's memory of the war from her mind.
(A) leak (B) erase (C) pile (D) process

_____ 3. People who attend this event have the _____ to win a free plane ticket to Japan.
(A) eyesight (B) imagination (C) opportunity (D) dinosaur

_____ 4. I love this song so much. Could you turn the _____ up, please?
(A) volume (B) threat (C) dairy (D) pill

_____ 5. Adapted from the fairy tale, this _____ show is suitable for children.
(A) tablet (B) pail (C) chance (D) puppet

Level 3 Test 3

Class: ________ No.: ________ Name: ________ Score: ________

I. 文意字彙 (40%)

________ 1. Do you know who i______ted the sewing machine?

________ 2. The professor w______ned the student against doing the dangerous experiment.

________ 3. The beaches are severely p______ed by the litter the vacationers left.

________ 4. To a______e his life goal, Leo works hard day and night.

________ 5. The idea of going overseas to study has never a______led to me.

II. 字彙配合 (請忽略大小寫) (40%)

(A) permission (B) considerable (C) conclusion (D) leopard (E) cheerful

_____ 1. A _____ cannot change its spots.

_____ 2. A _____ number of people gathered at Time Square to greet the New Year.

_____ 3. All the guests stood up and danced to the _____ music.

_____ 4. Did your father give you _____ to use his car?

_____ 5. In _____, I would like to thank those who have helped and supported me.

III. 選擇題 (20%)

_____ 1. This land was _____ for housing, not for industrial use.

(A) dipped (B) staffed (C) zoned (D) tapped

_____ 2. A bomb _____ on the MRT, killing many passengers.

(A) journeyed (B) exploded (C) attracted (D) quit

_____ 3. The test revealed the _____ of alcohol in the driver's blood.

(A) presence (B) permission (C) definition (D) learning

_____ 4. Everyone stood up and proposed a toast to the _____ and groom.

(A) cabin (B) bribe (C) straw (D) dip

_____ 5. _____ trees are one of tropical plants.

(A) Leopard (B) Tap (C) Staff (D) Palm

Level 3 Test 4

Class: ________ No.: ________ Name: ________ Score: ________

I. 文意字彙 (40%)

________ 1. Tony attended the meeting as a r____e of the workers. He spoke on behalf of them.

________ 2. Many good i____rs get ideas for their creations from their experiences in daily lives.

________ 3. Lucas s____ped off his clothes and excitedly jumped into the lake.

________ 4. The student was punished for dropping l____r in the classroom.

________ 5. We should use modern t____es to preserve the traditional crafts.

II. 字彙配合 (請忽略大小寫) (40%)

(A) stubborn	(B) extreme	(C) creative	(D) previous	(E) crispy

_____ 1. Mr. Brown is as _____ as a mule, never listening to others.

_____ 2. The freshly fried chicken is very juicy and _____.

_____ 3. Children always have _____ ideas which surprise the adults around them.

_____ 4. _____ to the invention of the telephone, people had to send messages to each other by letters or telegrams.

_____ 5. People are suffering from _____ weather, such as hurricanes and heat waves.

III. 選擇題 (20%)

_____ 1. Everyone has equal rights in a(n) _____ society.
(A) diverse (B) democratic (C) affordable (D) adventurous

_____ 2. Mr. Lin _____ his students to interview for colleges.
(A) chills (B) junks (C) removes (D) coaches

_____ 3. Janice washed the _____ off her boots before going into the house.
(A) extreme (B) background (C) adventure (D) dirt

_____ 4. Kevin decided to quit his job and moved to Japan for _____ reasons.
(A) probable (B) various (C) crispy (D) chill

_____ 5. There's a strong _____ that Mia could succeed because she worked so hard.
(A) probability (B) delegate (C) campus (D) pineapple

Level 3 Test 5

Class: ________ No.: ________ Name: ________ Score: ________

I. 文意字彙 (40%)

________ 1. My yearly s____y is less than one million dollars.

________ 2. The manager will take r____y for the mistake.

________ 3. The student is d____t. She even cheats on exams.

________ 4. It is a pity that Peter hasn't b____ted from his experience.

________ 5. Neil Armstrong, known as the first man to walk on the moon, is a____ed by many people all over the world.

II. 字彙配合 (請忽略大小寫) (40%)

(A) chilly	(B) decades	(C) profits	(D) normal	(E) casual

____ 1. The Internet, which plays an important role in our daily lives, was invented ____ ago.

____ 2. The businessman promised to donate some of his ____ to the charity.

____ 3. Jenny felt ____ when she went outside on the very cold night.

____ 4. The IT company allows employees to wear ____ clothes such as jeans and T-shirts.

____ 5. It is ____ for babies to cry to express their feelings.

III. 選擇題 (20%)

____ 1. The company put a(n) ____ for part-time workers on its website.
(A) advertisement (B) limb (C) fortune (D) structure

____ 2. Some youth are ____ about their future owing to the economic depression.
(A) colorful (B) anxious (C) normal (D) chilly

____ 3. All the baseball players ____ very well in the competition.
(A) performed (B) released (C) tuned (D) faded

____ 4. Did the police have any ____ against the suspect?
(A) advertising (B) luggage (C) jewel (D) proof

____ 5. Betty got completely ____ after drinking too much wine, so her friends called a taxi for her.
(A) worried (B) casual (C) drunk (D) formal

Level 3 Test 6

Class: ________ No.: ________ Name: ________ Score: ________

I. 文意字彙 (40%)

________ 1. Most of the people in the city are a____e of air pollution but don't know what they can do to solve the problem.

________ 2. The shark in the movie was very s____y. Some kids burst out crying upon seeing it.

________ 3. Ang Lee has had s____t success in his career as a director.

________ 4. I think offering discounts is an e____t way of increasing sales in the store.

________ 5. Mr. Baker worked very hard so that his family could live in c____t.

II. 字彙配合 (請忽略大小寫) (40%)

(A) vivid	(B) magical	(C) tight	(D) dosed	(E) chatted

____ 1. People in the town believe that the witch has the ____ powers to cure diseases.

____ 2. The collar of my shirt is too ____; I can hardly breathe.

____ 3. The scene is so ____ in my mind. It seems to have happened yesterday.

____ 4. Matthew ____ happily with his best friends in the restaurant.

____ 5. The doctor ____ me with a bottle of cough syrup because I had a bad cough.

III. 選擇題 (20%)

____ 1. Mia couldn't have retrieved the two pieces of ____ without the help of the hotel housekeeper.

(A) consolation (B) suicide (C) jewelry (D) sake

____ 2. After the tornado passed, nothing ____ of the fruit farm.

(A) remained (B) disliked (C) dosed (D) fancied

____ 3. The police are still searching the company for ____ to the identity of the thief.

(A) purses (B) clues (C) budgets (D) dislikes

____ 4. Financial experts worried that the disease would affect the ____ economy.

(A) pure (B) plastic (C) enchanting (D) global

____ 5. Low-cost ____ like Jetstar and AirAsia have become popular with people recently.

(A) airlines (B) missions (C) chats (D) doses

Level 3 Test 7

Class: ________ No.: ________ Name: ________ Score: ________

I. 文意字彙 (40%)

______ 1. The public are confident that the president of the bank is c______e of solving the financial crisis.

______ 2. The businessman is filled with a______n to become rich, famous, and powerful.

______ 3. Fanny's mother didn't a______e of her learning to drive. She thought Fanny was still too young.

______ 4. The r______e village is inaccessible by bus. You have to walk to get there.

______ 5. The depressed young man has difficulty dealing with his e______l problems.

II. 字彙配合 (請忽略大小寫) (40%)

(A) downtown	(B) product	(C) summit	(D) label	(E) cradle

______ 1. The ______ on the coat tells me that I should always have it dry-cleaned.

______ 2. The scientist's new invention is the ______ of ten years' research and hard work.

______ 3. The presidents of eight countries were invited to attend the ______ meeting.

______ 4. Alexander chose to live in the ______ area to save time from commuting.

______ 5. The father gently rocked the ______ and hummed a lullaby for his baby.

III. 選擇題 (20%)

______ 1. The temple is famous for a row of thick marble ______.
(A) goods (B) razors (C) columns (D) medals

______ 2. The second ______ lasts from February to June.
(A) republic (B) semester (C) wheat (D) breath

______ 3. The lifeguard ______ into the sea to save a drowning girl.
(A) dove (B) flashed (C) labeled (D) cradled

______ 4. Eva is a comedy actress with beautiful ______ lips.
(A) isolated (B) cherry (C) downtown (D) motor

______ 5. The art museum tightened ______ when the prime minister visited.
(A) wheat (B) breath (C) violence (D) security

Level 3 Test 8

Class: ________ No.: ________ Name: ________ Score: ________

I. 文意字彙 (40%)

________ 1. The customer service department has to deal with various c______ts every day.

________ 2. Ryan had r______led the secret to his wife before he died.

________ 3. Karen always c______es with her sister for their parents' attention.

________ 4. Hilary is s______ring from a bad cold. She feels unwell.

________ 5. Jennifer became a British c______n after living there for several years.

II. 字彙配合 (請忽略大小寫) (40%)

(A) suspect (B) information (C) apron (D) whistled (E) flooded

_____ 1. People living by the riverbank of the town were _____ out in the torrential storm.

_____ 2. The young man _____ happily when he was driving his car.

_____ 3. The guidebook contains all the _____ you may need when you study abroad.

_____ 4. The _____ of the robbery was finally under arrest after he had disappeared for days.

_____ 5. Remember to put on the _____ while cooking.

III. 選擇題 (20%)

_____ 1. The diligent reporter got _____ for the work she had done.
(A) taste (B) credit (C) lawn (D) flood

_____ 2. Leo makes _____ visits to Korea because his girlfriend lives there.
(A) suspicious (B) regional (C) doubtful (D) frequent

_____ 3. The CEO _____ the new project to his employees.
(A) announced (B) drained (C) flavored (D) whistled

_____ 4. Maya often uses moisturizing _____ for her dry hair.
(A) shampoo (B) medium (C) sink (D) chest

_____ 5. Being tall might be to your _____ to play basketball.
(A) announcement (B) neighborhood (C) advantage (D) drain

Level 3 Test 9

Class: ________ No.: ________ Name: ________ Score: ________

I. 文意字彙 (40%)

________ 1. The economy of the country is closely related to its t_____m.

________ 2. The little girl has a t_____t for music.

________ 3. All Linda's classmates don't like her because they cannot put up with her proud a_____e.

________ 4. The machine is powered by e_____y.

________ 5. Scientists have not found any c_____es on Mars so far.

II. 字彙配合 (請忽略大小寫) (40%)

(A) client	(B) relax	(C) liberty	(D) microwave	(E) dump

_____ 1. Food can be heated in a very short time in a _____.

_____ 2. Take a deep breath and try to _____. Things are not so bad.

_____ 3. It is against the law for factories to _____ waste into the rivers.

_____ 4. If you are at _____ to make comments, you can express your opinions.

_____ 5. The lawyer refuses to reveal any personal information of his _____ to the police.

III. 選擇題 (20%)

_____ 1. We provide customized services that are _____ to your needs.
(A) constant (B) armed (C) unique (D) ongoing

_____ 2. The police officer _____ the woman to put her hands in the air.
(A) folded (B) signaled (C) harbored (D) cabled

_____ 3. Owen decided to take the _____ Japanese course after the basic one.
(A) unarmed (B) continual (C) tasty (D) advanced

_____ 4. Queen Elizabeth was _____ at the age of twenty-five.
(A) crowned (B) microwaved (C) relaxed (D) dumped

_____ 5. The little boy likes to pat his puppy because its _____ is very soft.
(A) concert (B) liberty (C) fur (D) harbor

Level 3 Test 10

Class: ________ No.: ________ Name: ________ Score: ________

I. 文意字彙 (40%)

________ 1. The doctor a______ed me to take more rest.

________ 2. The art gallery is holding the largest Vincent van Gogh e______n.

________ 3. The robber t______ned the convenience store clerk with a gun.

________ 4. Do you know where the nearest dental c______c is? My tooth is aching.

________ 5. The popular TV program has drawn an a______e of two million viewers.

II. 字彙配合 (請忽略大小寫) (40%)

(A) hometown	(B) automatic	(C) sufficient	(D) miracle	(E) tropical

_____ 1. I don't have _____ time to finish the project.

_____ 2. The air conditioner has a(n) _____ temperature sensor.

_____ 3. It is important to protect the _____ rainforests from being damaged.

_____ 4. It's a(n) _____ that more than ten passengers have survived the plane crash.

_____ 5. Charlie went back to his _____, hoping to meet his childhood friends again.

III. 選擇題 (20%)

_____ 1. The historic temple was totally _____ in a fire.

(A) cropped (B) reminded (C) edited (D) destroyed

_____ 2. It is Alan's dream to travel to _____ space and watch the earth from another planet.

(A) outer (B) tropical (C) manual (D) costly

_____ 3. Ruby has a great sense of _____. She always makes us laugh with her jokes.

(A) silk (B) humor (C) pole (D) ash

_____ 4. We were asked to make a _____ of the two poems in the class.

(A) traveler (B) crop (C) crew (D) comparison

_____ 5. There are pairs of _____ celebrating Christmas in the Italian restaurant.

(A) miracles (B) poles (C) lovers (D) hometowns

Level 3 Test 11

Class: ________ No.: ________ Name: ________ Score: ________

I. 文意字彙 (40%)

________ 1. After being defeated in the election, the senator left the p______l party.

________ 2. Although Ben is very w______y, he is not happy at all.

________ 3. Bob started his teaching c______r right after he graduated from college.

________ 4. Against to all e______ns, our school team lost the basketball game.

________ 5. The violinist has t______l skills but not enough emotions.

II. 字彙配合 (請忽略大小寫) (40%)

(A) clown	(B) agriculture	(C) lung	(D) bacon	(E) sorrow

_____ 1. It is reported that smoking is closely related to _____ cancer.

_____ 2. Recently, the number of young people employed in _____ has grown.

_____ 3. A(n) _____ paints his face and dresses in a funny way.

_____ 4. Larry had toast and _____ for breakfast this morning.

_____ 5. The death of Queen Elizabeth II caused a great deal of _____ in the United Kingdom.

III. 選擇題 (20%)

_____ 1. Emily cannot stand the fast pace of _____ life. Instead, she enjoys the peace of rural life.
(A) frank (B) urban (C) expressive (D) dramatic

_____ 2. Everything about the movie star is _____ to her loyal fans.
(A) criminal (B) shy (C) attractive (D) frank

_____ 3. The new office building _____ behind our house.
(A) towers (B) reserves (C) educates (D) clowns

_____ 4. When traveling by car, Eric prefers to choose a _____, where he can park his car outside the room.
(A) motel (B) kingdom (C) cricket (D) reserve

_____ 5. The strong typhoon _____ us from going camping last week.
(A) clowned (B) prevented (C) reserved (D) educated

Level 3 Test 12

Class: ________ No.: ________ Name: ________ Score: ________

I. 文意字彙 (40%)

______ 1. The presidential e______n campaign will start at 10 a.m. tomorrow.

______ 2. The m______y of the citizens voted for Joe, so he was elected to be the president.

______ 3. In the past, the herbalists often e______ted on themselves to discover cures for diseases.

______ 4. Russia is the country with the biggest t______y in the world.

______ 5. The warning signs on the road have effectively d______ed traffic accidents.

II. 字彙配合 (請忽略大小寫) (40%)

(A) murdered (B) basement (C) designer (D) arrest (E) decorated

______ 1. "Freeze. You are all under _____," said the police to the bank robbers.

______ 2. To pay less rent, my friend chooses to live in the _____.

______ 3. My sister wants to be a fashion _____ in the future.

______ 4. On Double Tenth Day, the presidential hall was _____ with lights and the national flags.

______ 5. The police suspected that the old man did not die of a natural cause and that he might be _____.

III. 選擇題 (20%)

______ 1. Terry often _____ about the noise from his roommates.
(A) marches (B) engages (C) complains (D) squeezes

______ 2. The air _____ in this town was due to industrial emissions.
(A) cattle (B) pollution (C) variety (D) faith

______ 3. There will be no _____ charge for using the pool in this hotel. It is free for our guests during their stay.
(A) awful (B) routine (C) engaged (D) additional

______ 4. The naughty boy carved his initials on the _____ of that tree.
(A) squeeze (B) mayor (C) trunk (D) homicide

______ 5. The announcement of the pop singer's _____ shocked her fans.
(A) engagement (B) reduction (C) gap (D) minority

Level 3 Test 13

Class: ________ No.: ________ Name: ________ Score: ________

I. 文意字彙 (40%)

________ 1. At first, I thought someone must have stolen my wallet, but I found it b______h a pile of books later.

________ 2. An a______d silence spread, for the student failed to answer his teacher's question.

________ 3. The audience was i______sed by the excellent performance of the young pianist.

________ 4. My sister was vacuuming the floors. M______e, I was dusting the furniture.

________ 5. The book is a c______n of many famous love poems.

II. 字彙配合 (請忽略大小寫) (40%)

(A) desire	(B) twist	(C) stadium	(D) cone	(E) promote

_____ 1. A pop concert will be held in that _____ tonight.

_____ 2. If you don't warm up before exercise, you might easily _____ your ankle or arm.

_____ 3. The nun has no _____ for wealth. What she cares about is the welfare of the poor people.

_____ 4. The mother bought her son an ice cream _____ as a birthday treat.

_____ 5. The aim of this international organization is to _____ the welfare of mankind.

III. 選擇題 (20%)

_____ 1. Laws on equality should be passed to stop _____ discrimination.
(A) enjoyable (B) naked (C) racial (D) native

_____ 2. If you leave the metal outside in the rain, it will _____ easily.
(A) rust (B) detect (C) twist (D) encourage

_____ 3. Only the top _____ can win the gold medals in the tournament.
(A) athletes (B) elevators (C) democracies (D) webs

_____ 4. Ruby seems _____ that the typhoon might ruin her travel plan.
(A) bare (B) enjoyable (C) missing (D) fearful

_____ 5. After winning the game, Susie raised her arms in the air in a _____ of victory.
(A) theory (B) native (C) gesture (D) desire

Level 3 Test 14

Class: ________ No.: ________ Name: ________ Score: ________

I. 文意字彙 (40%)

________ 1. The young man in a black l_____r jacket looks cool on his shining new motorcycle.

________ 2. It has been raining for a whole week, and the m_____e in the air makes me uncomfortable.

________ 3. The national university is well-known for its academic e_____e.

________ 4. The injured soldier had an o_____n on his arm to remove a bullet.

________ 5. As long as we are students in this school, we are b_____d to follow its rules.

II. 字彙配合 (請忽略大小寫) (40%)

(A) banker	(B) bang	(C) determined	(D) mighty	(E) scarce

_____ 1. Ben was so angry that he closed the door with a _____.

_____ 2. The _____ waves overturned the small boat on the rough sea.

_____ 3. A _____ is one who manages a bank.

_____ 4. Job opportunities are _____ around the country now, and the unemployment rate keeps rising.

_____ 5. The girl is _____ to read as many comic books as she can this year.

III. 選擇題 (20%)

_____ 1. Cleo was so nervous about the exam that she _____ very early this morning.
(A) awoke (B) beamed (C) bound (D) graduated

_____ 2. Sam is not _____ with the neighborhood since he just moved here.
(A) fond (B) scarce (C) great (D) familiar

_____ 3. Dad reheated the soup in a saucepan on the _____.
(A) stove (B) underwear (C) necessity (D) professor

_____ 4. Peggy called the airline to _____ her plane ticket.
(A) rely (B) bang (C) deposit (D) confirm

_____ 5. Although the door was locked, the thief gained _____ to the house through a window in the yard.
(A) entry (B) tide (C) professor (D) stove

Level 3 Test 15

Class: ________ No.: ________ Name: ________ Score: ________

I. 文意字彙 (40%)

________ 1. Despite his back i____y, the soccer player insisted that he finish the game.

________ 2. Only a h____l of teachers agreed with the principal.

________ 3. High heat can kill harmful b____a. Be sure to cook the meat well done.

________ 4. Snow and water are the same s____es.

________ 5. The disease is so rare that most doctors do not r____e its symptoms.

II. 字彙配合 (請忽略大小寫) (40%)

(A) novelist	(B) union	(C) trend	(D) bloody	(E) bitter

____ 1. The ____ rose to fame because his latest book became a bestseller overnight.

____ 2. The scandal changed the ____ of public opinions.

____ 3. Emma has a ____ high school memory.

____ 4. The labor ____ suggested that the drivers should go on strike.

____ 5. Lucas was hit in the face by a ball and got a ____ nose.

III. 選擇題 (20%)

____ 1. The government should take measures to lower the crime ____.
(A) bay (B) import (C) rate (D) dime

____ 2. Walking on the dark street, the girl is ____ of being followed.
(A) conscious (B) elderly (C) moral (D) bare

____ 3. Ivy likes the new policy while her parents ____ differently.
(A) import (B) react (C) export (D) seize

____ 4. Bob always wears a dark suit on special ____.
(A) trends (B) scholarships (C) scientists (D) occasions

____ 5. When Ken made a ____ at Mom's arm, he fell down the stairs.
(A) union (B) bay (C) grab (D) novelist

Level 3 Test 16

Class: ________ No.: ________ Name: ________ Score: ________

I. 文意字彙 (40%)

______ 1. During high season, there won't be any v______t room at this popular hotel.

______ 2. Our teacher got a n______e "Superwoman" because she was always full of energy.

______ 3. The scientist is o______ving and recording all the details in his experiment.

______ 4. The man has a m______l disorder and should go to a psychiatrist for help.

______ 5. Jacky always b______es his classmates with some old jokes.

II. 字彙配合 (請忽略大小寫) (40%)

(A) screamed (B) optimistic (C) crashed (D) superior (E) scientific

______ 1. The success of the ______ experiment was a breakthrough in the history.

______ 2. My brother is ______ to me. He is good at many things.

______ 3. The bus ______ into a mountain, causing some deaths.

______ 4. Nancy ______ in terror when a man suddenly grabbed her handbag.

______ 5. Eric is ______ about the development of his company. He believes the business will prosper very soon.

III. 選擇題 (20%)

______ 1. Some ______ citizens like my grandparents live on social welfare.
(A) unoccupied (B) senior (C) junior (D) fairy

______ 2. Lisa turned to her professor for ______ on how to choose a thesis topic.
(A) reaction (B) honor (C) exchange (D) guidance

______ 3. Lavenders often ______ calmness and healing.
(A) represent (B) obey (C) brake (D) crash

______ 4. These soldiers were ______ for their bravery.
(A) yelled (B) exchanged (C) honored (D) healed

______ 5. The government provided a temporary shelter for the flood ______.
(A) beetles (B) donkeys (C) vehicles (D) victims

Level 3 Test 17

Class: ________ No.: ________ Name: ________ Score: ________

I. 文意字彙 (40%)

________ 1. If you are e______ring a new theory, you are studying or thinking about it very carefully.

________ 2. My family are decorating the living room, making p______ns for the coming Christmas.

________ 3. Kaity doesn't like to stay i______s on sunny days. She usually goes out to enjoy the sunshine.

________ 4. Clark rarely h______es when he has to make important decisions.

________ 5. The perfect l______n for the train station is the center of the city, which is easy to reach.

II. 字彙配合 (請忽略大小寫) (40%)

(A) violent (B) reliable (C) cupboard (D) bold (E) survey

_____ 1. Trust me! The news comes from a _____ source.

_____ 2. The _____ showed that only ten percent of people supported the new tax policy.

_____ 3. There is a _____ in the dining room where we usually put our dishes and plates.

_____ 4. When the _____ man walked on the rope between two skyscrapers, everyone held their breath.

_____ 5. A _____ earthquake struck Taiwan in 1999, causing extensive damage.

III. 選擇題 (20%)

_____ 1. Prices of smartphones _____ from store to store.
(A) inspect (B) vary (C) broadcast (D) analyze

_____ 2. According to the news, the criminal was sued in the _____ court.
(A) eager (B) civil (C) farther (D) odd

_____ 3. My bedroom is well _____ with everything neat and tidy.
(A) organized (B) skinny (C) dependable (D) fashionable

_____ 4. The jazz band will give a series of music _____ next month.
(A) cupboards (B) performances (C) captains (D) similarities

_____ 5. Our boss _____ that the project should be completed by the end of the week.
(A) surveyed (B) differed (C) organized (D) requested

Level 3 Test 18

Class: ________ No.: ________ Name: ________ Score: ________

I. 文意字彙 (40%)

________ 1. A helmet will give your head some p______n if you have a traffic accident.

________ 2. The hotel is not responsible for any damage to its guests' personal p______y.

________ 3. Pete witnessed a brave man helping the police c______e the bank robber today.

________ 4. The island is rich in natural r______es, such as forests, copper, and coal.

________ 5. The chef t______sed the pancake into the air and caught it in the pan.

II. 字彙配合 (請忽略大小寫) (40%)

(A) harmful	(B) humorous	(C) breast	(D) original	(E) visible

_____ 1. Those stars are hardly _____ to the naked eye.

_____ 2. The _____ by Picasso may be worth millions of dollars.

_____ 3. Using smartphones for a long time has a(n) _____ effect on people's eyesight.

_____ 4. Vivian has a check-up for _____ cancer twice a year.

_____ 5. A(n) _____ and easygoing person is always a good traveling companion.

III. 選擇題 (20%)

_____ 1. Several cows were _____ in the farm to prevent them from escaping.
(A) fueled (B) fenced (C) bombed (D) panicked

_____ 2. Just tell me directly. You don't need to beat around the _____.
(A) dealer (B) yolk (C) editor (D) bush

_____ 3. The police are _____ the cause of the explosion.
(A) panicking (B) bombarding (C) investigating (D) fueling

_____ 4. Ross passed a(n) _____ defense and got a master's degree last month.
(A) oral (B) unstable (C) solid (D) funny

_____ 5. When the fire alarm went off in the train, a wave of _____ spread through the passengers.
(A) onion (B) mosquito (C) panic (D) quality

Level 3 Test 19

Class: ______ No.: ______ Name: ______ Score: ______

I. 文意字彙 (40%)

______ 1. Oranges and tangerines are rich in v______n C.

______ 2. This gesture is not a______e in our country. Thus, you should avoid using it in public.

______ 3. Tina thinks the restaurant charges a r______e fee for its good service.

______ 4. In s______e of the bad weather, Steve still went camping in the mountains.

______ 5. The city council put up a life-size s______e of the great scientist in the park.

II. 字彙配合 (請忽略大小寫) (40%)

(A) industrial	(B) deck	(C) committee	(D) opposite	(E) tough

______ 1. The government set up a(n) ______ to study environmental protection.

______ 2. The waves washed over the ship's ______.

______ 3. Without good ______ relations, business cannot prosper.

______ 4. Tommy is kind and gentle, but his brother is quite the ______.

______ 5. The steak is too ______ to chew.

III. 選擇題 (20%)

______ 1. Cathy ______ and looked around before crossing the road.
(A) piloted (B) paused (C) funded (D) rid

______ 2. Paul and Irene had lunch together in the school ______, which served delicious food.
(A) deck (B) brick (C) cafeteria (D) stare

______ 3. Our ______ concern is to get the public aware of the environmental issue.
(A) immediate (B) electronic (C) tender (D) contrary

______ 4. Christopher was able to drive a jet ______ when he was young.
(A) muscle (B) committee (C) cleaner (D) fighter

______ 5. The government has set up a ______ to compensate earthquake victims.
(A) deck (B) painter (C) fund (D) kidney

Level 3 Test 20

Class: ________ No.: ________ Name: ________ Score: ________

I. 文意字彙 (40%)

________ 1. John is going s____y with a girl in his company and may get married soon.

________ 2. Gary b____ped into an old friend on the street this morning.

________ 3. The flags flapped gently in the b____e.

________ 4. Without enough income, we have to r____e living expenses.

________ 5. The custom can be t____ed back to the 16th century.

II. 字彙配合 (請忽略大小寫) (40%)

(A) kit	(B) organic	(C) inferior	(D) accurate	(E) emergency

____ 1. ____ farming is better for people's health and the environment.

____ 2. Push the button in case of ____, and then the door will open.

____ 3. The movie is a(n) ____ reflection of street vendors' daily lives.

____ 4. Oscar always feels ____ to his brother, who is taller and smarter than him.

____ 5. Todd is looking through his tool ____ for a screwdriver.

III. 選擇題 (20%)

____ 1. Daniel decided to build a(n) ____ swimming pool in his villa.
(A) outdoor (B) devout (C) constant (D) undesirable

____ 2. Hank spilled coffee on his shirt while he was giving it a ____.
(A) stir (B) strength (C) response (D) clip

____ 3. My niece only knew a limited ____ before entering preschool.
(A) palace (B) vocabulary (C) fist (D) kit

____ 4. Could you give me some ____ examples? Your explanation is too general.
(A) religious (B) desirable (C) specific (D) mobile

____ 5. There is time in ____ for us to make hamburgers.
(A) plenty (B) commotion (C) harm (D) weakness

Level 3 Test 21

Class: ________ No.: ________ Name: ________ Score: ________

I. 文意字彙 (40%)

________ 1. Kirk felt h_____l that he would get a promotion this time.

________ 2. Since the cake went s_____e, Maggie threw it away.

________ 3. The music app is very popular with the t_____e market.

________ 4. Melissa's beauty made her the e_____y of the others at the party.

________ 5. Although the fisherman tried hard to f_____t the old wooden boat, it sank in the end.

II. 字彙配合 (請忽略大小寫) (40%)

(A) gasoline (B) cooker (C) ladder (D) boots (E) twins

_____ 1. It is hard to prepare the meal without a _____.

_____ 2. Does the train run on _____?

_____ 3. The _____ look so alike. Most of their classmates can hardly tell one from the other.

_____ 4. It is raining heavily. You had better wear a pair of rain _____.

_____ 5. Mr. Miller was up a _____ to fix a leak in the roof of his house.

III. 選擇題 (20%)

_____ 1. We were _____ by the jazz band's performance.
(A) pumped (B) charmed (C) envied (D) drifted

_____ 2. _____ fish is a very popular dish in Japan.
(A) Appealing (B) Raw (C) Moist (D) Optimistic

_____ 3. Look! There's an eagle's _____ in the tree.
(A) nest (B) angel (C) disk (D) heater

_____ 4. Helen used some _____ to grow herbs and vegetables.
(A) stoves (B) jeeps (C) tubs (D) magnets

_____ 5. Many passengers were in a _____ to get on the train on New Year's Eve.
(A) boot (B) shrimp (C) rush (D) penguin

Level 3 Test 22

Class: ________ No.: ________ Name: ________ Score: ________

I. 文意字彙 (40%)

________ 1. The prime minister resigned because he made a h______e mistake in his economic policy.

________ 2. The weak patient f______ted in his room early this morning.

________ 3. Jessica is hard to get along with. She loses her t______r easily.

________ 4. If you are not satisfied with our product, you can return it with the r______t and get a full refund.

________ 5. I haven't seen him for some time. What has he been doing l______y?

II. 字彙配合 (請忽略大小寫) (40%)

(A) governor (B) coughing (C) punching (D) chimney (E) starving

____ 1. The man has been the state ____ for eight years.

____ 2. Joy has been ____ for two months. I think she needs to take an X-ray.

____ 3. The man was so angry that he kept ____ the wall.

____ 4. I am ____. Can we get something to eat?

____ 5. The ____ of the factory pours smoke into the air at night.

III. 選擇題 (20%)

____ 1. We decided to donate ____ of rice to those in need during holidays.
(A) sacks (B) ditches (C) flocks (D) nuns

____ 2. Nina likes to eat Italian food like ____ for dinner on Sundays.
(A) sin (B) brass (C) spaghetti (D) hell

____ 3. The two prisoners managed to ____ their way out of the prison.
(A) cough (B) tunnel (C) multiply (D) jet

____ 4. Did the ____ come to clean our house last week?
(A) maid (B) penny (C) punch (D) slip

____ 5. The population continues to ____ in that town because of the immigration policy.
(A) unite (B) flock (C) starve (D) multiply

Level 3 Test 23

Class: ________ No.: ________ Name: ________ Score: ________

I. 文意字彙 (40%)

________ 1. The man who lost his life while saving the drowning boy would be remembered for his b_____y.

________ 2. Did you g_____p the main idea of the passage?

________ 3. Many people have a h_____r of height. The best example is that they are afraid of going to the top of a tall building.

________ 4. You have to a_____e to Linda for hurting her feelings.

________ 5. There is no drinking f_____n in this park because of the COVID-19.

II. 字彙配合 (請忽略大小寫) (40%)

(A) helmet (B) mushrooms (C) marble (D) stings (E) receiver

_____ 1. The statue is carved out of a huge block of _____.

_____ 2. The customer angrily put down the _____ and refused to talk any more.

_____ 3. Bees and wasps have _____ in their tails.

_____ 4. Mr. Adams can identify poisonous _____ in the forest.

_____ 5. A _____ can protect your head when you fall.

III. 選擇題 (20%)

_____ 1. The old men who sell _____ tickets have been caught.
(A) underlying (B) fake (C) juicy (D) tough

_____ 2. The little boy tripped and _____ milk on the carpet of the restaurant.
(A) mushroomed (B) jumped (C) spilled (D) forged

_____ 3. We felt _____ after a switchback ride through mountains.
(A) tender (B) dizzy (C) uncountable (D) genuine

_____ 4. Matilda is good at cooking tomato _____ for pasta.
(A) sauce (B) pepper (C) oak (D) marble

_____ 5. The lady lifted her cup to the lips and had a(n) _____ of tea.
(A) vase (B) chin (C) sip (D) imitation

Level 3 Test 24

Class: ________ No.: ________ Name: ________ Score: ________

I. 文意字彙 (40%)

________ 1. Two nurses a______ted the doctor to perform the operation.

________ 2. It is a r______f to know that the missing boy has arrived home safely.

________ 3. Air that is h______d contains a lot of moisture.

________ 4. We always sleep in a t______t when we go camping.

________ 5. The lake f______e hard at such a low temperature.

II. 字彙配合 (請忽略大小寫) (40%)

(A) brunch	(B) hint	(C) dock	(D) stitching	(E) skating

_____ 1. On Sunday morning, I usually skip breakfast and eat _____ instead.

_____ 2. A _____ is a place in a port where ships are loaded, unloaded, or repaired.

_____ 3. The girl was _____ on the frozen pond.

_____ 4. Gina is _____ some decorations onto the dress for the costume party.

_____ 5. The _____ to the question is not clear enough.

III. 選擇題 (20%)

_____ 1. Don't forget to turn off the _____ after use.
(A) saucer (B) pigeon (C) crab (D) faucet

_____ 2. Kevin _____ a lot of pieces off the rock.
(A) hinted (B) whirled (C) skated (D) chipped

_____ 3. Monica likes to watch Korean dramas in her _____ time.
(A) tap (B) unity (C) poetry (D) leisure

_____ 4. The police did not solve the _____ of the brutal murder of a homeless man.
(A) stitch (B) mystery (C) quote (D) spin

_____ 5. The little boy drew a picture of the forest with green and brown _____.
(A) markers (B) hints (C) skates (D) verses

Level 3 Test 25

Class: ________ No.: ________ Name: ________ Score: ________

I. 文意字彙 (40%)

________ 1. Michelle finds it hard to r____t the temptation of chocolate.

________ 2. In some fairy tales, a brave and handsome k____t would appear in time to save a beautiful lady from danger.

________ 3. The passengers are wondering whether the plane will take off in such s____y weather.

________ 4. The g____e effect is one of the causes of global warming.

________ 5. The dying man h____rs for a sight of his son.

II. 字彙配合 (請忽略大小寫) (40%)

(A) pills (B) outdoors (C) chopped (D) stole (E) naps

_____ 1. It was awful that many trees in the forest were _____ down.

_____ 2. The thief was caught. She _____ necklaces and rings.

_____ 3. Gina took some _____, hoping they would ease her bad headache.

_____ 4. Babies usually take several short _____ during the day.

_____ 5. The man had a dark tan because he worked _____ most of the time.

III. 選擇題 (20%)

_____ 1. Pauline likes to wear a wool _____ to keep warm in winter.
(A) crane (B) vest (C) sausage (D) feather

_____ 2. The visitors watched a school of _____ leaping out of the water.
(A) dolphins (B) buds (C) rags (D) chops

_____ 3. Some workers demanded higher _____ because of long working hours.
(A) assistants (B) historians (C) skis (D) wages

_____ 4. Several garden plants in my yard begin to _____ in spring.
(A) bud (B) crane (C) nap (D) oppose

_____ 5. The _____ of New Zealand is diverse, including rough coastlines, volcanic peaks, and glaciers.
(A) snooze (B) geography (C) starvation (D) lemonade

Level 3 Test 26

Class: ________ No.: ________ Name: ________ Score: ________

I. 文意字彙 (40%)

________ 1. At first g____e, the woman standing by the door looked like my English teacher.

________ 2. The player is t____l to the people around her to give her support.

________ 3. S____t 5 from 12 and you get 7.

________ 4. In the United States, many families have more than one a____e.

________ 5. I am worried about my father because he smokes a pack of c____es a day.

II. 字彙配合 (請忽略大小寫) (40%)

(A) icy	(B) ripe	(C) lettuce	(D) holy	(E) warmth

____ 1. Jake sliced some ____ and tomatoes and mixed them up to make some salad.

____ 2. A temple is considered to be a(n) ____ place.

____ 3. The street vendor greeted her guests with ____.

____ 4. If you want to eat the bananas, you need to wait until they are ____.

____ 5. The ____ road is very slippery so you must be careful when walking on it.

III. 選擇題 (20%)

____ 1. My classmate ____ at me when I walked into the classroom.
(A) steamed (B) crawled (C) untied (D) grinned

____ 2. Can you check the cake in the ____ to see if it is cooked thoroughly?
(A) oven (B) lettuce (C) scale (D) pint

____ 3. Eva and Fred are ____ at using social media to connect with their friends.
(A) mature (B) freezing (C) skillful (D) divine

____ 4. There is still a ____ of hope that the trapped miners are alive.
(A) knot (B) donut (C) firework (D) ray

____ 5. Would you like a slice of ____ for dessert?
(A) melon (B) buffalo (C) glimmer (D) navy

Level 3 Test 27

Class: ________ No.: ________ Name: ________ Score: ________

I. 文意字彙 (40%)

________ 1. The short-tempered man often f_____es with anger for no reason.

________ 2. The children left the shop happily, l_____king their ice cream.

________ 3. There will be a grand b_____t after the wedding ceremony. The guests can eat anything they like there.

________ 4. Some explorers got lost in the desert and died of t_____t.

________ 5. Ann puts on a woolen s_____f to keep her neck warm.

II. 字彙配合 (請忽略大小寫) (40%)

(A) koala	(B) volleyball	(C) horns	(D) suburbs	(E) imports

_____ 1. Do you prefer _____ or basketball?

_____ 2. The country tries very hard to reduce its reliance on _____ by supporting the local businesses.

_____ 3. A(n) _____ is an animal, native to Australia.

_____ 4. The Whites own a house in the _____ of Taipei.

_____ 5. The male goat has very long _____ on its head.

III. 選擇題 (20%)

_____ 1. Tim and his sister are movie addicts. They go to the _____ twice a month.
(A) sleeve (B) cinema (C) waterfall (D) recorder

_____ 2. The professional golfer won the championship and covered herself in _____.
(A) glory (B) drag (C) rot (D) possibility

_____ 3. The snowman we made last night _____ in the sunlight.
(A) decomposed (B) melted (C) exported (D) sketched

_____ 4. Stan Lee and Steve Ditko are the _____ of Spider-Man.
(A) avenues (B) creators (C) horns (D) pits

_____ 5. Jack drew a(n) _____ of the bridge and then gave it color.
(A) import (B) craving (C) grocery (D) outline

Level 3 Test 28

Class: ________ No.: ________ Name: ________ Score: ________

I. 文意字彙 (40%)

________ 1. What's the h______y pay of the part time work?

________ 2. I got a s______f back after I had sat at my desk for over eight hours.

________ 3. The chandelier takes one hundred 60-watt light b______bs.

________ 4. There is a hole in the wall. I must have it m______ded.

________ 5. R______r has it that the young actor got married secretly.

II. 字彙配合 (請忽略大小寫) (40%)

(A) indoor	(B) glow	(C) sucking	(D) flashlight	(E) threading

_____ 1. The policeman patrolled the dark streets with a(n) _____ in hand.

_____ 2. While walking at the beach this evening, I was attracted to the beauty of the _____ of the setting sun.

_____ 3. The designer was _____ sea shells on a string to make a necklace.

_____ 4. The baby was _____ his thumb.

_____ 5. There is a(n) _____ pool in the community, so people can use it in all seasons.

III. 選擇題 (20%)

_____ 1. Tom brushed his teeth so hard that his _____ hurt.
(A) scissors (B) laces (C) dragonflies (D) gums

_____ 2. The singer has a(n) _____ figure and a beautiful face.
(A) overseas (B) outdoor (C) playful (D) slender

_____ 3. My grandfather used to keep a lot of _____ for farm work.
(A) rectangles (B) oxen (C) weapons (D) loaves

_____ 4. Half of _____ in this town were in favor of a ban on gambling.
(A) voters (B) shoelaces (C) circuses (D) threads

_____ 5. We must be _____ to the danger of drunk driving.
(A) laced (B) glowed (C) awakened (D) fixed

Level 3 Test 29

Class: ________ No.: ________ Name: ________ Score: ________

I. 文意字彙 (40%)

________ 1. When traveling, people may carry some b____e.

________ 2. The searching team used modern equipment, trying to l____e the sunken ship.

________ 3. To my r____t, I have to give up my plan.

________ 4. The scientist won't stop until he gets a s____y result in his experiment.

________ 5. On hearing the funny joke, the audience burst into l____r.

II. 字彙配合 (請忽略大小寫) (40%)

(A) slices	(B) plugs	(C) golf	(D) pal	(E) sum

_____ 1. To make the dish, Miranda cut a potato into thin _____.

_____ 2. Jack usually plays _____ with his manager every weekend.

_____ 3. Pulling out the _____ of household appliances can save electricity.

_____ 4. Sue was left a large _____ of money by her aunt.

_____ 5. When I have free time, I like to go online and chat with my cyber _____.

III. 選擇題 (20%)

_____ 1. Jessica went to the _____ to dye her hair blonde.
(A) weave (B) wagon (C) housekeeper (D) hairdresser

_____ 2. Mike keeps his wallet in the _____ pocket of his jacket.
(A) inner (B) cheery (C) acceptable (D) merry

_____ 3. Because of the downpour, my clothes were wet and my hair was _____.
(A) damming (B) golfing (C) dripping (D) plugging

_____ 4. The _____ of the kiwi fruit tastes a little bit sour.
(A) clay (B) flesh (C) studio (D) bull

_____ 5. Amy had learned how to _____ clothes before she got married.
(A) slice (B) sum (C) weave (D) thumb

Level 3 Test 30

Class: ________ No.: ________ Name: ________ Score: ________

I. 文意字彙 (40%)

________ 1. The suspect is trying hard to prove that he is i____t.

________ 2. The p____n is trying every possible way to win votes from the public.

________ 3. The government will take some measures to r____t the sale of cigarettes.

________ 4. I have a s____n that my colleagues are trying to get rid of me.

________ 5. The tourist plans to w____r slowly through a local market in Italy.

II. 字彙配合 (請忽略大小寫) (40%)

(A) drowned	(B) summary	(C) gossip	(D) wiped	(E) slope

____ 1. The teacher asked her students to write a ____ of the article.

____ 2. Andy was nearly ____ when he was little. Therefore, he dreads going into the water.

____ 3. The swimmer ____ his body dry with a big towel.

____ 4. The village is on the ____, overlooking the lake.

____ 5. I heard a piece of juicy ____ that Fay was dating her ex-boyfriend again.

III. 選擇題 (20%)

____ 1. As soon as Liam saw his daughter, he gave her a big ____.
(A) hug (B) dare (C) hallway (D) slope

____ 2. Eunice is a shopaholic. Her ____ is full of clothes and accessories.
(A) bait (B) closet (C) flour (D) log

____ 3. Jason likes reading. He decides to ____ a bookshelf to the wall.
(A) screw (B) loosen (C) pad (D) embrace

____ 4. Ivy is getting into trouble. Her life is a ____.
(A) pancake (B) bullet (C) pad (D) mess

____ 5. Owen keeps his ____ in his account to resist overspending.
(A) inclines (B) savings (C) notebooks (D) laundries

Level 3 Test 31

Class: ________ No.: ________ Name: ________ Score: ________

I. 文意字彙 (40%)

______ 1. A p____e was held with everyone walking down the street to celebrate the victory of the war.

______ 2. We will not feel relieved before the murderer is arrested and sent to j____l.

______ 3. A recent p____l showed that eighty percent of college students are worried that they may not be able to find jobs after they graduate.

______ 4. Paul s____e that he would never drink again after the accident. I hope he will keep his word.

______ 5. The shirt was so large that it hung l____e on Betty's slim body.

II. 字彙配合 (請忽略大小寫) (40%)

(A) hammer	(B) ribbon	(C) snapped	(D) bunch	(E) surrounded

______ 1. The little girl tied up her hair with a red ______.

______ 2. One of the strings of his violin ______ when he was performing.

______ 3. My mom asked me to buy a ______ of grapes for her on my way home.

______ 4. My father drove a nail into the wall with a ______.

______ 5. The village is ______ by forests. Thus, people cannot see it from outside.

III. 選擇題 (20%)

______ 1. According to the weather forecast, there would be ______ showers in the evening.
(A) scattered (B) slack (C) darling (D) nearby

______ 2. Many foreign tourists buy medicine and cosmetics at ______ in Japan.
(A) flutes (B) barns (C) grasshoppers (D) drugstores

______ 3. Ian ______ the bathroom floor with a brush after taking a shower.
(A) imprisoned (B) scrubbed (C) clothed (D) hummed

______ 4. The host spoke into a ______ at the awards ceremony.
(A) pat (B) procession (C) lifetime (D) microphone

______ 5. As a car enthusiast, Ryan ______ his sports car twice a month.
(A) pounds (B) waxes (C) snaps (D) disperses

Level 3 Test 32

Class: ________ No.: ________ Name: ________ Score: ________

I. 文意字彙 (40%)

______ 1. The heavy workload has w______ned the manager's health. Her health goes from bad to worse.

______ 2. I will visit my aunt s______e next week, but I'm not sure what day it is.

______ 3. The audience r______red with laughter at the host's funny words.

______ 4. All the classmates don't have the f______giest idea about how to solve the question.

______ 5. The couple finally got divorced after a five-year s______n.

II. 字彙配合 (請忽略大小寫) (40%)

(A) survivor (B) permit (C) sword (D) dash (E) missile

_____ 1. You'd better _____ for the platform because your train is going to leave in three minutes.

_____ 2. The knight drew his _____ and began to fight with his enemy.

_____ 3. The soldiers are going to launch a _____ in ten minutes.

_____ 4. In the United States, you can apply for a learner's _____ to learn how to drive before you get a driver's license.

_____ 5. The man was the only _____ of the airplane crash.

III. 選擇題 (20%)

_____ 1. Olivia wiped away her sweat with a _____.
(A) rooster (B) handkerchief (C) lighthouse (D) missile

_____ 2. We have _____ up the packages to send before leaving Paris.
(A) strengthened (B) permitted (C) rushed (D) parceled

_____ 3. Justin receives a _____ of love letters from his secret admirers.
(A) dash (B) bundle (C) hut (D) sword

_____ 4. Mindy bought a lot of fluffy toys and gift _____ for her son's birthday party.
(A) wrap (B) tobacco (C) porcelain (D) jazz

_____ 5. To make the wine mature quickly, Manson put it in oak _____.
(A) scholars (B) winners (C) barrels (D) cocks

Level 3 Test 33

Class: ________ No.: ________ Name: ________ Score: ________

I. 文意字彙 (40%)

________ 1. I cannot sleep well because I've got an a_____e in my back.
________ 2. The Internet is h_____y for collecting information in a short time.
________ 3. To s_____e up her retired life, Gina immigrates to Portugal.
________ 4. We discussed the topic "s_____l harassment" in class today.
________ 5. Maggie is always j_____s of the lifestyle of her rich cousin.

II. 字彙配合 (請忽略大小寫) (40%)

(A) harvest (B) portion (C) tag (D) mall (E) mob

_____ 1. The military troops were called in to control the angry _____ who were causing trouble in the capital city.
_____ 2. Owing to good weather conditions, farmers are expecting a good _____.
_____ 3. The shopping _____ consists of various shops and restaurants.
_____ 4. The price _____ of the skirt shows its worth.
_____ 5. Charles has to spend a large _____ of his income paying the rent.

III. 選擇題 (20%)

_____ 1. The insurer's reputation has been harmed because its online _____ was hacked.
(A) dumpling (B) tag (C) database (D) cocktail
_____ 2. Tina and her family stopped at a(n) _____ to have dinner on their way home.
(A) inn (B) bead (C) harvest (D) swan
_____ 3. The researcher always _____ himself in his studies every day.
(A) mobs (B) buries (C) seals (D) portions
_____ 4. The chef _____ the duck until it was golden brown.
(A) roasted (B) parroted (C) hurt (D) wed
_____ 5. Although Mr. Styles lost the mayoral election, his _____ wanted him to run for the president.
(A) tons (B) spices (C) followers (D) seals

Level 3 Test 34

Class: ________ No.: ________ Name: ________ Score: ________

I. 文意字彙 (40%)

________ 1. People usually drill a small hole on a c____t and have its juice.

________ 2. I have to have my car i____ted twice a year.

________ 3. The first landing on the moon is one of the most important events in the history of m____d.

________ 4. Commuting by MRT is a s____e choice in a busy city.

________ 5. The witch turned the handsome prince into an ugly b____t.

II. 字彙配合 (請忽略大小寫) (40%)

(A) passengers (B) sweat (C) dust (D) weeds (E) posters

_____ 1. To keep their house neat and tidy, Ted vacuums the floors and his children _____ all the furniture once a week.

_____ 2. The regulation is that all _____ in vehicles must fasten the seat belts.

_____ 3. The hard exercise made me _____.

_____ 4. My sister put up some _____ of her favorite actor on the wall of the bedroom.

_____ 5. One of the gardener's jobs is to remove _____ from the garden.

III. 選擇題 (20%)

_____ 1. After the police completed the investigation into the robbery, the truth about this crime _____.
(A) examined (B) perspired (C) dawned (D) dusted

_____ 2. Patrick put the fresh lobsters in the _____ to preserve them better.
(A) placard (B) trader (C) freezer (D) hanger

_____ 3. The constant _____ of the old fan is really annoying.
(A) pine (B) buzz (C) daybreak (D) hay

_____ 4. The Buddhist _____ has lived alone in the mountains for ten years.
(A) monk (B) poster (C) spinach (D) lily

_____ 5. Kelly was once my financial _____, who helps me manage my money.
(A) hanger (B) jelly (C) adviser (D) weed

Level 3 Test 35

Class: ________ No.: ________ Name: ________ Score: ________

I. 文意字彙 (40%)

________ 1. The population of the town has s____k in recent years.

________ 2. The meeting was p____ed because of the boss's illness.

________ 3. The banquet was great, and the guests all had a m____s day.

________ 4. To donate a small amount of money to charity is a good d____d.

________ 5. The band was playing some l____y music, which made me feel like dancing.

II. 字彙配合 (請忽略大小寫) (40%)

(A) joyful	(B) hasty	(C) collar	(D) alley	(E) inspector

____ 1. Chinese New Year is a(n) ____ occasion for children because they can receive red envelopes then.

____ 2. Mary made a(n) ____ decision to marry Zack, whom she had known for only two months.

____ 3. Zoe is afraid of walking in the dark ____ alone at night.

____ 4. The ticket ____ checked my ticket to ensure that I have paid the fare.

____ 5. Max pulled up the ____ of his overcoat to protect his neck from the cold wind.

III. 選擇題 (20%)

____ 1. Fanny doesn't like to wear boots with high ____.
(A) shadows (B) tanks (C) monsters (D) heels

____ 2. The bad news cast a(n) ____ over the meeting. All the members were worried.
(A) shadow (B) berry (C) pitch (D) echo

____ 3. Tyler ate the soup but ____ it out immediately because he found it had gone bad.
(A) swelled (B) spit (C) wept (D) grew

____ 4. My friends and I got such a ____ and lost power when we saw the mouse.
(A) gorge (B) swell (C) collar (D) fright

____ 5. The little girl ____ her school bag behind her.
(A) heeled (B) sobbed (C) trailed (D) shadowed

Level 3 Test 36

Class: ________ No.: ________ Name: __________ Score: __________

I. 文意字彙 (40%)

________ 1. The students all s____hed with relief when the teacher said no one failed the math exam.

________ 2. A group of tourists talked excitedly in the hotel l____y.

________ 3. Some people look attractive on the outside, but they are quite s____w.

________ 4. It is a p____y that the talented director died young.

________ 5. Hong Kong was once a British c____y.

II. 字彙配合 (請忽略大小寫) (40%)

(A) robe (B) tray (C) meadow (D) swift (E) monthly

____ 1. We should take ____ action to stop the gossip spreading.

____ 2. The waitress brought my dinner on a ____.

____ 3. I missed the time when I lived in the country where I could run and play with my friends in the ____.

____ 4. Lillian wrapped a ____ around herself after taking a shower.

____ 5. You can save a bit of money if you buy a ____ train ticket.

III. 選擇題 (20%)

____ 1. The baseball player was arrested because he helped ____ on the game.
(A) hire (B) bet (C) deepen (D) frighten

____ 2. Julie's wrecked car was ____ away to a nearby garage.
(A) towed (B) splashed (C) whipped (D) elbowed

____ 3. My mom has fitted a red ____ in the living room.
(A) carpet (B) almond (C) hatchway (D) sidewalk

____ 4. The man didn't take orders from people who were ____ to him.
(A) superficial (B) junior (C) monthly (D) deep

____ 5. We were ____ by a call when watching the basketball game on TV.
(A) hatched (B) paved (C) interrupted (D) rented

Level 3 Test 37

Class: ________ No.: ________ Name: ________ Score: ________

I. 文意字彙 (40%)

________ 1. The public t_____t of this city is very convenient.

________ 2. I visited several h_____c sites in the old city.

________ 3. Don't always say yes to your kids, or you'll s_____l them.

________ 4. The basketball player's nose began to b_____d when another player hit his face hard by accident.

________ 5. I would like to have ice cream for d_____t.

II. 字彙配合 (請忽略大小寫) (40%)

(A) carriages (B) sincere (C) wicked (D) gallons (E) tribes

_____ 1. There's a _____ witch in this fairy tale.

_____ 2. Many people drove horse-drawn _____ to the West during the Gold Rush.

_____ 3. Amis is one of the indigenous _____ in Taiwan.

_____ 4. I want to express my _____ apology for the inconvenience caused by my mistake.

_____ 5. The tank is filled with ten _____ of oil.

III. 選擇題 (20%)

_____ 1. Who will the citizens _____ for president?
(A) lock (B) elect (C) ruin (D) deliver

_____ 2. We should make our lives more _____ by helping others.
(A) wicked (B) alphabetic (C) hateful (D) meaningful

_____ 3. Instead of accepting the _____ to my birthday party, Lily turned it down.
(A) tribe (B) invitation (C) lock (D) comma

_____ 4. Koalas and _____ are native to Australia.
(A) kangaroos (B) shepherds (C) peas (D) moths

_____ 5. The government decided to launch more _____ into outer space.
(A) alphabets (B) portraits (C) rockets (D) powders

Level 3 Test 38

Class: ________ No.: ________ Name: ________ Score: ________

I. 文意字彙 (40%)

________ 1. What are the e______ts that make up the air we breathe?

________ 2. The waitress p______red some water into the glass on the table.

________ 3. The young screenwriter tried to sell his script to a film p______r.

________ 4. People in an i______y tower know little about the difficulties of ordinary lives.

________ 5. The bribery scandal of the politician hit the h______es today.

II. 字彙配合 (請忽略大小寫) (40%)

(A) skipped (B) sprayed (C) blessed (D) romantic (E) shiny

_____ 1. The candle light gave the room a _____ atmosphere.

_____ 2. Don't touch the plant. I just _____ insecticide on it.

_____ 3. I _____ over the chapters which were not important.

_____ 4. I hope my children are _____ with health, wisdom, and diligence.

_____ 5. I think Tina's _____ black hair is very beautiful.

III. 選擇題 (20%)

_____ 1. Jess can't play the guitar, but she is a good _____ player in our band.
(A) lollipop (B) keyboard (C) cart (D) napkin

_____ 2. In winter, the temperature here can drop to _____ twenty.
(A) bright (B) confused (C) minus (D) amazed

_____ 3. It was a _____ for me to quit my current job and start my YouTuber career.
(A) gamble (B) trolley (C) peanut (D) troop

_____ 4. The complicated railroad system in Tokyo is really _____.
(A) incredible (B) tricky (C) confusing (D) romantic

_____ 5. _____ a lion is not an easy task for ordinary people.
(A) Skipping (B) Astonishing (C) Taming (D) Widening

Level 3 Test 39

Class: ________ No.: ________ Name: ________ Score: ________

I. 文意字彙 (40%)

________ 1. President Lincoln declared that all the s______es in the United States were free in 1863.

________ 2. Zoe p______ded that everything was fine, but actually she was depressed.

________ 3. Asia is the largest c______t on Earth.

________ 4. The old man is the former French a______r to Canada.

________ 5. The kidnappers tied the boy's w______ts and feet to prevent him from escaping.

II. 字彙配合 (請忽略大小寫) (40%)

(A) pronounce (B) tug (C) rotten (D) dim (E) cast

_____ 1. In the _____ light of the street lamp, I could hardly see things clearly.

_____ 2. The fisherman _____ the line to the middle of the river.

_____ 3. The _____ eggs gave out a bad smell.

_____ 4. I don't know how to _____ this foreign name. No matter how hard I try, it just doesn't sound right.

_____ 5. I have to _____ my dog back lest it would chase the letter carrier.

III. 選擇題 (20%)

_____ 1. The distance between my home and the bus stop is two _____.
(A) headquarters (B) kilometers (C) blouses (D) lords

_____ 2. The construction sound _____ on Jessica's nerves.
(A) jarred (B) ganged (C) lengthened (D) tugged

_____ 3. Sylvia felt _____ for Taiwan when she first went to Brazil.
(A) homesick (B) bright (C) neat (D) rotten

_____ 4. Frank is good at playing several instruments such as _____ and violin.
(A) emperor (B) misery (C) pearl (D) trumpet

_____ 5. To our surprise, the captain has worked as an enemy _____.
(A) poverty (B) cast (C) spy (D) tangerine

Level 3 Test 40

Class: ________ No.: ________ Name: ________ Score: ________

I. 文意字彙 (40%)

________ 1. My parents hired a t_____r to teach me English at home.

________ 2. After the snow melted, the road became muddy and s_____y.

________ 3. Call an a_____e. We should send the injured man to the hospital right away.

________ 4. I finally got a h_____p of homework done.

________ 5. Being a tour guide is a challenging job. You must be e_____c and enthusiastic.

II. 字彙配合 (請忽略大小寫) (40%)

(A) champion	(B) teasing	(C) honesty	(D) shoveling	(E) garage

_____ 1. What did you get in the _____ sale?

_____ 2. The world chess _____ is a 21-year-old young woman.

_____ 3. Wilson is _____ the snow away in the garden.

_____ 4. Stop _____ the poor boy about his ragged clothes.

_____ 5. _____ is the best policy.

III. 選擇題 (20%)

_____ 1. The clothes shop offers a _____ of ten percent on cash purchases.
(A) discount (B) bar (C) kindergarten (D) magician

_____ 2. Messi was _____ as one of the best football players in the world.
(A) misted (B) peeled (C) yelled (D) ranked

_____ 3. Alexander bought a new _____ to put his comic books and magazines in.
(A) bookcase (B) controller (C) necktie (D) spade

_____ 4. All of the guests were asked to rub their shoes against the _____ in the doorway before getting into the house.
(A) skin (B) class (C) shovel (D) rug

_____ 5. The heavyweight boxer punched her opponent in the _____.
(A) reduction (B) jaw (C) champion (D) dishonesty

Level 4 Test 1

Class: ________ No.: ________ Name: ________ Score: ________

I. 文意字彙 (40%)

________ 1. Many people expressed their s____y for the orphans who lost their parents in the war.

________ 2. Ken l____hed into some illegal business and soon got into big trouble.

________ 3. At the i____l stage of the project, we have to discuss the costs.

________ 4. Sam couldn't e____e the pain in his injured leg, so he began to moan and weep.

________ 5. Eli tells me about her terrible experience in c____e, so I can't share it with you.

II. 字彙配合 (請忽略大小寫) (40%)

(A) protein	(B) alert	(C) enthusiasm	(D) severe	(E) protest

____ 1. The earthquake did ____ damage to the village and caused many houses to collapse.

____ 2. In spite of his height, Paul never loses his ____ for playing basketball.

____ 3. The boy turned off TV, got up from the sofa and went back to his room under ____.

____ 4. We must take in a certain amount of ____ in order to be healthy and strong.

____ 5. The soldier was asked to be ____ to every possible danger.

III. 選擇題 (20%)

____ 1. Jeff took three days' leave with his boss's ____.
(A) intelligence (B) approval (C) creativity (D) harmony

____ 2. Sue ____ all the obstacles and achieved her ambition to run her own business.
(A) overcame (B) strengthened (C) protested (D) consisted

____ 3. The restaurant serves ____ Mexican cuisine.
(A) habitual (B) fragile (C) authentic (D) harsh

____ 4. It's crucial to develop a ____ relationship with nature.
(A) first (B) genuine (C) vulnerable (D) harmonious

____ 5. Kathy held a party to celebrate her parents' thirtieth wedding ____.
(A) paragraph (B) margin (C) anniversary (D) context

Level 4

Level 4 Test 2

Class: ________ No.: ________ Name: ________ Score: ________

I. 文意字彙 (40%)

________ 1. The i____e anxiety made Fiona suffer from a stomach disorder.

________ 2. In this album, the singer b____ds jazz and rap into his own musical style.

________ 3. The soldiers faced great r____e when they attacked the small village.

________ 4. How to promote e____y between men and women at workplace is the key issue at the conference.

________ 5. James eventually achieved his goal through c____s efforts.

II. 字彙配合 (請忽略大小寫) (40%)

(A) experimental	(B) depression	(C) research	(D) maturity	(E) artificial

____ 1. Dr. Black is doing ____ on the influence of the mass media on public opinions.

____ 2. The cookies manufactured in our factory do not contain any ____ additives.

____ 3. The high school differs from other schools in its ____ forms of teaching.

____ 4. Jim lacks ____ in handling money matters. He still needs more experience to do the work better.

____ 5. Many countries around the world are working together to overcome the worst economic ____ in history.

III. 選擇題 (20%)

____ 1. The extreme hot weather in the desert is barely ____ to some tourists.
(A) digital (B) fake (C) psychological (D) tolerable

____ 2. Isabella kept her earrings and necklaces in an unbreakable ____.
(A) container (B) analysis (C) household (D) quotation

____ 3. The nursing home is mainly funded by voluntary ____ from all walks of life.
(A) handwriting (B) oxygen (C) contribution (D) depression

____ 4. Scientists from Europe and America work together in the chemical ____.
(A) donation (B) gallery (C) laboratory (D) householder

____ 5. Ordinary people are not allowed to carry ____ in Taiwan.
(A) quotations (B) arms (C) surroundings (D) licenses

Level 4 Test 3

Class: ________ No.: ________ Name: ________ Score: ________

I. 文意字彙 (40%)

________ 1. The writer often conveys concerns of u_____l interest. That's why her books always sell well.

________ 2. The police were urged to take immediate m_____es to stop crimes.

________ 3. The dog is f_____ned to the pole when its owner is not at home.

________ 4. Mia's rude behavior was not a_____e for such a formal occasion.

________ 5. When asked about the fight at the bar, Bill said he was too drunk to remember the i_____t.

II. 字彙配合 (請忽略大小寫) (40%)

(A) essential (B) maximum (C) hardship (D) route (E) brutal

_____ 1. To save time, we have to take the direct _____ to our destination.

_____ 2. The boat can carry a(n) _____ of thirty passengers. If it is overloaded, it will be in danger.

_____ 3. After the taxi driver got crippled in an accident, he suffered incredible _____ for the rest of his life.

_____ 4. Fertile soil, abundant rainfall, and sunlight are all _____ to a good harvest.

_____ 5. Someone released a video which showed _____ physical punishment in a cram school.

III. 選擇題 (20%)

_____ 1. The celebrity was flat _____ after the investment failed.
(A) conventional (B) keen (C) broke (D) dispensable

_____ 2. Yvonne _____ with her roommates in cleaning the kitchen.
(A) cooperated (B) contributed (C) established (D) routed

_____ 3. The Halloween party ended in _____ because the restaurant was on fire.
(A) machinery (B) tragedy (C) reference (D) keenness

_____ 4. The birth rate is very low in this _____.
(A) community (B) disability (C) psychologist (D) gene

_____ 5. Anyone who breaks the traffic rules will face _____.
(A) establishments (B) organizations (C) penalties (D) necessities

Level 4

Level 4 Test 4

Class: ________ No.: ________ Name: ________ Score: ________

I. 文意字彙 (40%)

________ 1. The judge gave very c_____e criticism about the contestants' performance.

________ 2. The calm lake is so beautiful with the surrounding mountains r_____ted in it.

________ 3. The young lady was proved g_____y of robbery and caught by the police.

________ 4. People's bad b_____r in public such as littering and spitting is very annoying.

________ 5. Blood v_____ls are the narrow tubes through which your blood flows.

II. 字彙配合 (請忽略大小寫) (40%)

(A) convince	(B) percentage	(C) install	(D) estimate	(E) fetch

_____ 1. The engineers will _____ air-conditioners in all the classrooms.

_____ 2. A(n) _____ was that 11,200 families suffered big losses of their property in the devastating floods.

_____ 3. One of the tricks my dog can do is to _____ the ball for me.

_____ 4. The survey revealed the _____ of college graduates who cannot get employment.

_____ 5. Jill failed to _____ the teacher of her honesty.

III. 選擇題 (20%)

_____ 1. Charlotte asked her children to be quiet, but they were not very _____.
(A) tragic (B) ethnic (C) cooperative (D) athletic

_____ 2. Robert had difficulty finding a _____ for his new book.
(A) publisher (B) canoe (C) battery (D) landscape

_____ 3. Harper lacks _____ and seldom involves herself in school club activities.
(A) fetch (B) motivation (C) humanity (D) economics

_____ 4. We can watch the broadcast of the FIFA World Cup via _____.
(A) ethnics (B) ships (C) satellite (D) makeup

_____ 5. David likes to _____ along the river through the gorges in fall.
(A) canoe (B) persuade (C) bring (D) landscape

Level 4 Test 5

Class: ________ No.: ________ Name: ________ Score: ________

I. 文意字彙 (40%)

________ 1. Dan planted a seed and made a close o____n about its growth.

________ 2. The film shocked the world when it shows how war prisoners were treated with c____y.

________ 3. Salmon spend most of their lifetime in the ocean but come back to the rivers to b____d.

________ 4. The public are not satisfied with the recent economic r____ms.

________ 5. Hang in there. The e____l success will be worth the efforts you have made.

II. 字彙配合 (請忽略大小寫) (40%)

(A) atmosphere	(B) identical	(C) numerous	(D) genius	(E) annual

____ 1. To our surprise, Joyce and I bought Dad gifts that were ____.

____ 2. The damp ____ of the cave made it difficult for us to breathe.

____ 3. After reading Ted's best-selling novel, the readers all regard him as a(n) ____.

____ 4. The city holds their ____ music festival in May. If you miss it, you will have to wait for another year.

____ 5. In the history of mankind, we can find ____ examples of tragedy caused by greed.

III. 選擇題 (20%)

____ 1. The city ____ decided to build a civic sports center near the station.
(A) cargo (B) council (C) fiction (D) memorial

____ 2. All of us have ____ confidence in the coach's judgment.
(A) predictable (B) argumentative (C) absolute (D) influential

____ 3. The couple often ____ over money matters after their baby was born.
(A) interpreted (B) transformed (C) predicted (D) quarreled

____ 4. The winning of this award has great ____ to the singer. It means that her album has been recognized.
(A) non-fiction (B) significance (C) communication (D) genius

____ 5. The computer ____ urgently recalled all the defective products.
(A) manufacturer (B) fact (C) cargo (D) consumer

Level 4

Level 4 Test 6

Class: ________ No.: ________ Name: ________ Score: ________

I. 文意字彙 (40%)

________ 1. When Sue tried to open the door, the k____b came off in her hand.

________ 2. With only a m____e income, the couple can only manage to make both ends meet but cannot afford a vacation abroad.

________ 3. The trailer for the movie aroused my c____y , making me eager to know what happened next.

________ 4. I haven't decided yet; therefore, I cannot give you a d____e answer.

________ 5. Teenagers tend to r____l against their elders because they want to assert themselves.

II. 字彙配合 (請忽略大小寫) (40%)

(A) attraction	(B) contest	(C) evidence	(D) application	(E) ignorance

____ 1. Ed's ridiculous comments showed his ____ of the current situation.

____ 2. It was a close ____ since the two teams were equally competitive.

____ 3. There is some ____ to suggest that drinking green tea daily is good for health.

____ 4. It's difficult for many teenagers to resist the ____ of online games.

____ 5. You had better fill in the ____ form and send it in by the end of the month.

III. 選擇題 (20%)

____ 1. There was a lot of ____ of the director's speech.
(A) construction (B) evidence (C) criticism (D) tremble

____ 2. Mr. Li prepared extra materials to ____ intellectual interest in his students.
(A) absorb (B) spark (C) contest (D) deserve

____ 3. Helicopters and troops will be transported by a freight ____ tomorrow.
(A) carrier (B) cabinet (C) merit (D) prime

____ 4. The volunteers from different countries helped deliver food to the ____ in Ukraine.
(A) strengths (B) intentions (C) cupboards (D) refugees

____ 5. According to the weather forecast app, it will be cloudy with ____ showers tomorrow.
(A) flexible (B) rigid (C) occasional (D) main

Level 4 Test 7

Class: ________ No.: ________ Name: ________ Score: ________

I. 文意字彙 (40%)

________ 1. A m______e choice examination shows several possible answers for you to choose from.

________ 2. Mrs. Wang is going to have a s______y for lung cancer tomorrow.

________ 3. The c______y provides food, clothing, and shelter to the homeless.

________ 4. A m______r brought a letter to the commander this morning.

________ 5. A total eclipse of the sun is a rare natural p______n which you may see only once in your lifetime.

II. 字彙配合 (請忽略大小寫) (40%)

(A) triumph	(B) declare	(C) celebration	(D) competition	(E) recall

_____ 1. We will be in _____ with the top players, so we should practice hard.

_____ 2. When will the judge _____ the winner of the contest?

_____ 3. The little girl believes that good will _____ over evil in the end.

_____ 4. We are going to invite some friends for a barbecue in our backyard in _____ of Moon Festival.

_____ 5. The man looks quite familiar, but I cannot _____ his name.

III. 選擇題 (20%)

_____ 1. We had such a good time at the party that we were _____ to leave.
(A) adequate (B) reluctant (C) triumphant (D) independent

_____ 2. No matter how hard Sandy tries, there is no _____ that she will win a contract.
(A) guarantee (B) desperation (C) categorization (D) offense

_____ 3. Trapped in the net, the pig made _____ efforts to escape.
(A) productive (B) desperate (C) willing (D) dependent

_____ 4. The following examples _____ how pop music influences the development of teenage culture today.
(A) interact (B) recollect (C) illustrate (D) delight

_____ 5. In this country, drug possession is a(n) _____ that can carry the death penalty.
(A) exception (B) fossil (C) legend (D) offense

Level 4

Level 4 Test 8

Class: ________ No.: ________ Name: ________ Score: ________

I. 文意字彙 (40%)

______ 1. I tried to help him out with his work; n______s, he turned me down.

______ 2. Sam was so badly injured that a full r______y seemed to be impossible.

______ 3. The situation was very u______t, and so many patients were rushed to the emergency room.

______ 4. The c______e of the building resulted from the huge earthquake.

______ 5. Alice is quiet and shy, in sharp c______t to her outgoing sister.

II. 字彙配合 (請忽略大小寫) (40%)

(A) invested (B) representation (C) opposed (D) admission (E) convention

______ 1. The club held its annual ______ in the hall.

______ 2. Cleo wore a black scarf as a(n) ______ of her mourning for her husband's death.

______ 3. The company has ______ a large sum of money in the project.

______ 4. Zoe is very happy because she has obtained the ______ to her ideal college.

______ 5. Many teachers and students ______ the new examination system for its injustice.

III. 選擇題 (20%)

______ 1. Gabriel ______ to win the speech contest because his story was the most touching.
(A) deserved (B) differentiated (C) referred (D) displayed

______ 2. We marveled at the ______ of the band's live performance.
(A) confession (B) investment (C) magnificence (D) immigrant

______ 3. Ed was born color-blind, so he has difficulty ______ between red and green.
(A) referring (B) distinguishing (C) exhibiting (D) disordering

______ 4. Eventually, Vanessa ______ the other opponents in the singing reality show.
(A) defeated (B) contrasted (C) collapsed (D) framed

______ 5. The package may contain ______ materials and must be handled with care.
(A) explosive (B) circular (C) disorderly (D) miserable

Level 4 Test 9

Class: ________ No.: ________ Name: ________ Score: ________

I. 文意字彙 (40%)

________ 1. In order to strengthen diplomatic relations, the M______r of Foreign Affairs will visit several European countries next week.

________ 2. As the ship was sinking, the captain had no choice but to a______n it.

________ 3. It is better to make hotel r______ns in advance when you travel during high season.

________ 4. Viola received h______h criticism for a minor mistake.

________ 5. Helen gave a flat r______l to Tim's invitation because he wasn't her type.

II. 字彙配合 (請忽略大小寫) (40%)

(A) gender (B) overlook (C) monitor (D) detective (E) exposure

_____ 1. The wife hired a private _____ to spy on her husband.

_____ 2. The security guard checked the _____ to see if any stranger had come.

_____ 3. A baby's _____ can be known by the end of the fourth month of pregnancy.

_____ 4. Without good health, we cannot do anything, so we mustn't _____ the importance of health.

_____ 5. The plant needs enough water and _____ to the sun.

III. 選擇題 (20%)

_____ 1. Billy was happy about the _____ of his dream of being a lawyer.
(A) creation (B) investigation (C) fulfillment (D) infant

_____ 2. The _____ situation got worse in the shadow of the COVID-19 pandemic.
(A) detective (B) promising (C) distinguished (D) economic

_____ 3. Jim and Kate had no children, so they decided to _____ a baby.
(A) adopt (B) defend (C) monitor (D) transfer

_____ 4. Lydia introduced me to her former _____ Sara at the Christmas party.
(A) literature (B) colleague (C) civilization (D) gender

_____ 5. Under enemy _____, the city of one million people suffered badly.
(A) civilization (B) occupation (C) adoption (D) creation

Level 4 Test 10

Class: ________ No.: ________ Name: ________ Score: ________

I. 文意字彙 (40%)

________ 1. The boy was p____ted by sheer curiosity to peep through the keyhole.

________ 2. The kind man agreed to help me without a moment's h____n.

________ 3. Before you start to make a cake, you must have all the i____ts ready and put them on the kitchen counter.

________ 4. Lisa was shocked when she learned that her son was i____ed in the illegal activity.

________ 5. Sold at a c____e price, this action camera is the hottest item in the store.

II. 字彙配合 (請忽略大小寫) (40%)

(A) objective (B) durable (C) defense (D) agency (E) abstract

____ 1. You should learn to be more ____ and listen to others' opinions.

____ 2. Howard got the job through an employment ____.

____ 3. A house built of stone is ____ and it lasts much longer than a wooden one.

____ 4. Martin Luther King made speeches in ____ of the rights of the black.

____ 5. What the speaker said was so ____ that few people understood.

III. 選擇題 (20%)

____ 1. All Della wants is not a mansion but a(n) ____ house with a small yard.
(A) overnight (B) immediate (C) modest (D) needy

____ 2. To ensure safety, there is a speed ____ in the school areas.
(A) generation (B) restriction (C) distribution (D) impact

____ 3. The ____ of the damage caused by the tsunami is still unknown now.
(A) participation (B) objective (C) classification (D) extent

____ 4. Being confident in yourself is the best way to deal with ____ pressure among your friends.
(A) species (B) defense (C) peer (D) agency

____ 5. The new policy aims to ____ congestion and reduce the volume of the traffic.
(A) relieve (B) provoke (C) differ (D) entail

Level 4 Test 11

Class: ________ No.: ________ Name: ________ Score: ________

I. 文意字彙 (40%)

________ 1. The parents were accused of n______ting their three-year-old child, who had been left alone at home for a whole day.

________ 2. A m______t is a structure which is built in memory of an important person or event.

________ 3. The secret agent disguised himself as a Russian by speaking with a Russian a______t.

________ 4. Mia can't go abroad now since she forgot to r______w her passport.

________ 5. Simon decided to p______e his dream after graduating.

II. 字彙配合 (請忽略大小寫) (40%)

(A) appreciation (B) defensive (C) isolation (D) diligent (E) philosophy

_____ 1. Taking advantage of every opportunity is my _____ of life.

_____ 2. The _____ employee seized every opportunity to learn in the big company.

_____ 3. We are allowed to use _____ weapons in some situations.

_____ 4. Being a newcomer in the neighborhood, Sam had a strong feeling of _____.

_____ 5. Peter wrote a thank-you letter to his professor in _____ of his support.

III. 選擇題 (20%)

_____ 1. Lena's excuse for being late is not very _____. We don't think the manager will buy it.

(A) coarse (B) persuasive (C) inspiring (D) offensive

_____ 2. Daniel _____ his schedule so that he could make time to travel.

(A) adjusted (B) consulted (C) retreated (D) paced

_____ 3. Joseph took out car _____ when he bought a new sports car.

(A) insurance (B) facility (C) dynasty (D) rebellion

_____ 4. The story of Helen Keller _____ many people to never give up when faced with challenges.

(A) adapted (B) inspired (C) insured (D) advanced

_____ 5. I met people from _____ backgrounds and origins while working abroad.

(A) diverse (B) hard-working (C) smooth (D) defensive

Level 4 Test 12

Class: ________ No.: ________ Name: ________ Score: ________

I. 文意字彙 (40%)

________ 1. The restaurant has a bad r_____n for poor service though its food is delicious and inexpensive.

________ 2. The teacher told Billy to r_____e his essay before he handed it in.

________ 3. Washing your hands frequently will prevent i_____n.

________ 4. It is of critical importance to pass a law against child l_____r.

________ 5. Although everything looked normal, my i_____t told me that something went wrong.

II. 字彙配合 (請忽略大小寫) (40%)

(A) passive	(B) efficiency	(C) dominant	(D) aspect	(E) mysterious

_____ 1. Annie was almost perfect in every _____ so she was elected as a leader.

_____ 2. The woman passed away in _____ circumstances.

_____ 3. English is the _____ language of the world.

_____ 4. Only those who work with _____ can finish the project on time.

_____ 5. _____ smoking may lead to lung cancer.

III. 選擇題 (20%)

_____ 1. Toronto is chosen as one of the most livable cities in the world because of its _____ climate.
(A) mild (B) opposing (C) ashamed (D) occupied

_____ 2. The speeding motorcycle went through a red light with a police car in _____.
(A) efficiency (B) intuition (C) pursuit (D) rainfall

_____ 3. Ben is often _____ by his teacher because he is a noise maker.
(A) occupied (B) accessed (C) demonstrated (D) disciplined

_____ 4. Only ten _____ of the employees got a bonus last year.
(A) contrary (B) percent (C) point (D) aspect

_____ 5. Emily's _____ into Harvard Medical School pleased her parents.
(A) discipline (B) reverse (C) acceptance (D) comedy

Level 4 Test 13

Class: ________ No.: ________ Name: ________ Score: ________

I. 文意字彙 (40%)

________ 1. The pop singer had to travel in d____e because there were too many fans around.

________ 2. Besides academic work, these high schools also put e____s on sports in their teaching.

________ 3. There are a couple of spelling errors here; o____e, it is a good piece of writing.

________ 4. The r____ns were once temples one thousand years ago.

________ 5. It is interesting that my mother r____es a famous movie star.

II. 字彙配合 (請忽略大小寫) (40%)

(A) permanent (B) outcome (C) pessimistic (D) forecast (E) objection

____ 1. The ____ of the election will be announced until all the votes are counted.

____ 2. These graduates are quite ____ about their career prospects.

____ 3. Leo made a(n) ____ to my proposal. He said it was impractical.

____ 4. Sandra gave up a(n) ____ job and became a freelancer.

____ 5. Before going hiking, you had better check the weather ____.

III. 選擇題 (20%)

____ 1. Mia ____ her letter to her son so that nobody could read it except him and herself.
(A) conveyed (B) coded (C) stressed (D) wrecked

____ 2. The police suspected that the death of the politician was not ____, so they decided to conduct a closer investigation.
(A) temporary (B) elementary (C) accidental (D) bankrupt

____ 3. After reconstruction, the village has changed beyond ____.
(A) recognition (B) reduction (C) commerce (D) assistance

____ 4. Alice wants to buy a(n) ____ computer which can be easily carried when she is on business.
(A) dense (B) portable (C) gloomy (D) instructive

____ 5. The huge loss would ____ the technology company.
(A) issue (B) instruct (C) predict (D) bankrupt

Level 4 Test 14

Class: ________ No.: ________ Name: ________ Score: ________

I. 文意字彙 (40%)

________ 1. When you learn diving, you must do what the diving i____r tells you to do.

________ 2. The scientists have conducted extensive research on genetic e____g for years.

________ 3. According to the law, the president has the a____y over the military.

________ 4. The oppressed people wanted to o____w the cruel ruler so much.

________ 5. The audience stood up and applauded the o____g performance of the musician.

II. 字彙配合 (請忽略大小寫) (40%)

(A) resign	(B) eliminate	(C) destruction	(D) concentrate	(E) formula

____ 1. My brother cannot ____ on his study when he is hungry.

____ 2. There is no magic ____ that can help you get rich overnight.

____ 3. The overweight patient was asked to ____ dessert from his diet.

____ 4. The explosion caused the ____ of the buildings in the area.

____ 5. The scandal forced the government official to ____ from his post.

III. 選擇題 (20%)

____ 1. The police attempted to ____ their objective of reducing the crime rate.
(A) manage (B) accomplish (C) dismiss (D) plot

____ 2. Please handle the ____ vase with care. If it falls, it may break into pieces.
(A) determined (B) possible (C) delicate (D) literary

____ 3. The beautiful ____ of Alishan attracts many tourists from other countries.
(A) preservative (B) scenery (C) inspiration (D) dismissal

____ 4. This island has great ____ for wind power.
(A) potential (B) elimination (C) capitalism (D) delicacy

____ 5. Ariel made a New Year's ____ to quit sugar.
(A) photography (B) formula (C) resolution (D) theme

Level 4 Test 15

Class: ________ No.: ________ Name: ________ Score: ________

I. 文意字彙 (40%)

________ 1. Senior members can enjoy all p______es of club membership.

________ 2. Ivy r______ded her son with a book for behaving well.

________ 3. After a fierce battle, the soldiers defeated the enemy and held down the f______t.

________ 4. My grandparents chose to live in a rural d______t owing to the quietness of the countryside.

________ 5. The carpenter c______ed the wood into the shape of a horse.

II. 字彙配合 (請忽略大小寫) (40%)

(A) alcohol (B) interaction (C) visual (D) financial (E) scoop

_____ 1. My daughter wants one _____ of strawberry ice cream.

_____ 2. Pictures and films are _____ aids often used by many teachers.

_____ 3. To solve his _____ problems, Mike has to have two jobs.

_____ 4. Terry's doctor told him to keep away from _____ and cigarettes.

_____ 5. It is found that there is a lack of _____ between parents and children nowadays.

III. 選擇題 (20%)

_____ 1. Bella was arrested for _____ the wanted criminal in her house.
(A) portraying (B) visualizing (C) digesting (D) sheltering

_____ 2. We learn to express our own opinions through active _____ in class discussion.
(A) participation (B) accuracy (C) catastrophe (D) biology

_____ 3. The Internet celebrity's _____ personality won him ten thousand followers in a few weeks.
(A) intellectual (B) primitive (C) enormous (D) magnetic

_____ 4. People were dancing to the _____ of the music at the party.
(A) summary (B) rhythm (C) disaster (D) era

_____ 5. Classical music plays a _____ role in this musician's life.
(A) prominent (B) visual (C) modern (D) financial

Level 4 Test 16

Class: ________ No.: ________ Name: ________ Score: ________

I. 文意字彙 (40%)

________ 1. The user m_____l will tell you what you should do in setting up a computer step by step.

________ 2. Doing voluntary work may help you develop a close b_____d with your community.

________ 3. The new sports center will be fully f_____l next month.

________ 4. Emma's new novel went to number one on the best-seller list shortly after the p_____n of it.

________ 5. The school authorities held a c_____n against drugs.

II. 字彙配合 (請忽略大小寫) (40%)

(A) acid	(B) evaluate	(C) tribal	(D) peculiar	(E) dispute

_____ 1. The investor disguised himself as a guest to _____ the service in the hotel.

_____ 2. The problem of racism is not _____ to this country only. The problem exists in other countries too.

_____ 3. _____ rain is considered a threat to the environment.

_____ 4. Ralph's parents always _____ with each other over money issues.

_____ 5. Some ancient _____ customs are unique and sometimes surprising.

III. 選擇題 (20%)

_____ 1. The night market is rapidly _____ into a tourist attraction with booming tourism.
(A) scratching (B) interfering (C) expanding (D) assessing

_____ 2. After his grandmother passed away, Jack took _____ of her house.
(A) intensity (B) economy (C) conscience (D) possession

_____ 3. Jessica was so _____ that she spilled coffee on her colleague's skirt.
(A) clumsy (B) utilitarian (C) automatic (D) rural

_____ 4. Our teacher _____ us in grammar by giving us a lot of repetitive practice.
(A) campaigned (B) drilled (C) meddled (D) scratched

_____ 5. With many years of hard work, the model has finally won worldwide _____ and fame.
(A) privacy (B) dispute (C) sculpture (D) popularity

Level 4 Test 17

Class: ________ No.: ________ Name: ________ Score: ________

I. 文意字彙 (40%)

________ 1. You must check every single detail of the contract before putting your s______e to it.

________ 2. All the people at the construction s______e must wear helmets to protect their heads.

________ 3. The witness made a p______e description of the robber, so the police were able to catch him in a short time.

________ 4. The dose of medicine works better in c______n with a glass of warm water.

________ 5. After the treatment, there's only a s______t improvement in the patient's condition. What a disappointing result!

II. 字彙配合 (請忽略大小寫) (40%)

(A) volunteer (B) capacity (C) explosion (D) status (E) ensure

____ 1. Ten people got killed in the ____ of the gas stove in the bakery.

____ 2. Fresh ingredients almost ____ a tasty dish.

____ 3. Mr. and Mrs. Kao ____ to help the poor every weekend.

____ 4. The gas tank has a(n) ____ of a thousand gallons.

____ 5. Pedro tried hard to achieve higher social ____.

III. 選擇題 (20%)

____ 1. The science fiction series has a large ____ in many countries.
(A) conservative (B) circulation (C) minimum (D) polish

____ 2. Mia is a ____ person, who enthusiastically participates in outdoor activities.
(A) realistic (B) dynamic (C) facial (D) lousy

____ 3. Laura buys some exercise books to improve her ____ performance.
(A) traditional (B) academic (C) distinct (D) exact

____ 4. Derek took a(n) ____ course in Japanese for his business trip to Japan.
(A) stocky (B) energetic (C) furious (D) intensive

____ 5. Our ____ in Seoul deals with all our business in Korea.
(A) satisfaction (B) transportation (C) agent (D) status

Level 4

Level 4 Test 18

Class: ________ No.: ________ Name: __________ Score: __________

I. 文意字彙 (40%)

______ 1. There will be more functions after the s______e updates.

______ 2. The vegetable vendor has donated a lot of money to the charity, and many people are deeply touched by her g______y.

______ 3. Adam had s______y got home when it began to rain.

______ 4. The actress refused to c______t on her new love affair.

______ 5. Kenting National Park is proud of p______sing one of the most beautiful beaches in Taiwan.

II. 字彙配合 (請忽略大小寫) (40%)

(A) concrete	(B) formation	(C) consistent	(D) prevention	(E) mutual

____ 1. The students were taught about the ____ of clouds in the science class.

____ 2. Ann and I have a ____ interest in gardening. We both love planting plants and flowers.

____ 3. Crime ____ is the main goal of the new government.

____ 4. What Tim says is often not ____ with what he does.

____ 5. The police have ____ evidence about who robbed the bank.

III. 選擇題 (20%)

____ 1. The movie director rose to ____ as soon as his first movie was released.
(A) concrete (B) fame (C) formation (D) electronics

____ 2. Under no ____ should you do anything illegal.
(A) intimates (B) forerunners (C) circumstances (D) viruses

____ 3. In search of her roots, Ava wants to find out where her ____ came from.
(A) submarines (B) recipes (C) ancestors (D) devices

____ 4. This five-star hotel is regarded as one of the most ____ hotels in Singapore.
(A) solar (B) mutual (C) intimate (D) luxurious

____ 5. With years of practice, Sophia ____ amazing skills in badminton.
(A) concreted (B) acquired (C) distributed (D) revealed

Level 4 Test 19

Class: ________ No.: ________ Name: ________ Score: ________

I. 文意字彙 (40%)

________ 1. The social vulnerable groups are struggling to s_____e jobs.

________ 2. Read the table of c_____ts and you'll know what the book is about.

________ 3. Everybody must follow a certain p_____e to apply for a visitor visa.

________ 4. Diana could not get a job here, so she went e_____e to try her luck.

________ 5. The TV station decided to prolong the show after having received positive f_____k from the viewers.

II. 字彙配合 (請忽略大小寫) (40%)

(A) apparent (B) concentration (C) invention (D) promotion (E) suspicious

_____ 1. The singer offered her autographs to her fans as part of the _____ of her latest album.

_____ 2. The _____ of the car has made an enormous change in people's lives.

_____ 3. Peter found a(n) _____ package on the train and reported it to the police.

_____ 4. The speech was so boring that we lost _____ and fell asleep during it.

_____ 5. Look at the dark clouds in the sky. It is _____ that it will rain soon.

III. 選擇題 (20%)

_____ 1. Though Mr. Lin is busy, he still _____ some time to play Switch games with his daughter every week.

(A) spares (B) invades (C) demands (D) constructs

_____ 2. Ethan is a(n) _____ boy. He always adjusts himself to the new environment soon.

(A) suspicious (B) authentic (C) obvious (D) adaptable

_____ 3. Aurora used recycled materials in the _____ of eco-friendly blankets.

(A) tortoise (B) manufacture (C) earnest (D) graduation

_____ 4. Be sure to visit our _____ to find out more about our fitness courses.

(A) composition (B) website (C) concentration (D) invention

_____ 5. With great effort, Mason made _____ progress in playing the piano.

(A) remarkable (B) adaptable (C) demanding (D) false

Level 4 Test 20

Class: ________ No.: ________ Name: ________ Score: ________

I. 文意字彙 (40%)

________ 1. It's difficult for me to i_____y with the main character in this movie.

________ 2. In Chinese culture, the dragon is usually a_____ed with the emperors.

________ 3. This news story is without f_____n and doesn't deserve our trust.

________ 4. Betty had a pleasant e_____r with her old friend, who she had lost contact with for decades.

________ 5. Ruby was frustrated because her marriage was beyond r_____y.

II. 字彙配合 (請忽略大小寫) (40%)

(A) invasion	(B) elastic	(C) profitable	(D) aggressive	(E) diversity

_____ 1. The string is _____. I can stretch it to tie up all the old newspapers.

_____ 2. The _____ dog always tries to bite anyone who passes by.

_____ 3. It is said that the crop circles are direct evidence of aliens' _____ of our planet.

_____ 4. While this business is quite _____, it is a high-risk investment. You may either become a millionaire or go bankrupt because of it.

_____ 5. To stay healthy, you must eat a(n) _____ of food.

III. 選擇題 (20%)

_____ 1. Hazel felt _____ to those who lost their families in an earthquake.
(A) essential (B) sympathetic (C) spiritual (D) basic

_____ 2. Carter taught his employees the _____ of time management.
(A) professionals (B) consequences (C) fundamentals (D) solutions

_____ 3. There is growing public _____ over the soaring gas prices.
(A) anxiety (B) invasion (C) opera (D) elastic

_____ 4. The new company policy has caused a _____ between the two departments.
(A) curse (B) split (C) proposal (D) marathon

_____ 5. Logan decided to try a(n) _____ therapy since he was too weak to have surgery.
(A) alternative (B) grateful (C) unprofitable (D) material

Level 4 Test 21

Class: ________ No.: ________ Name: ________ Score: ________

I. 文意字彙 (40%)

______ 1. Mike was attached to the Australian e____y at the age of thirty.

______ 2. The international company sells its products all over the g____e.

______ 3. It is really a magnificent sight when the sun e____es over the horizon.

______ 4. A capital city is usually more p____s than the others in a country.

______ 5. The s____r form of "lives" is "life."

II. 字彙配合 (請忽略大小寫) (40%)

(A) insert	(B) confusion	(C) cushion	(D) analyze	(E) chorus

______ 1. The government's changeable economic policy has caused the public _____.

______ 2. Nancy likes to lie on the sofa with a(n) _____ under her head.

______ 3. The survey was carried out to _____ consumers' online shopping habits.

______ 4. A(n) _____ is a group of people who sing together.

______ 5. The cashier is teaching an old man where to _____ his card and how to enter his code to withdraw cash from an ATM.

III. 選擇題 (20%)

______ 1. There is a _____ for secretary in the human resources department.
(A) choir (B) robber (C) syllable (D) vacancy

______ 2. The company was fined in relation to its _____ and false advertising.
(A) muddy (B) misleading (C) imaginative (D) leisurely

______ 3. Citizens _____ in front of the city call, demanding the mayor resign.
(A) analyzed (B) stabbed (C) praised (D) assembled

______ 4. The increasing _____ of car accidents worried local people.
(A) syllable (B) frequency (C) confusion (D) insert

______ 5. The celebrity was accused of stirring up religious _____.
(A) psychology (B) stab (C) bridegroom (D) hatred

Level 4

Level 4 Test 22

Class: ________ No.: ________ Name: ________ Score: ________

I. 文意字彙 (40%)

________ 1. Both soldiers and c______ns have become victims of the war.

________ 2. The actor amused the audience by giving i______ns of some singers.

________ 3. The college works in p______p with local businesses. Its graduates can apply to them for summer internship.

________ 4. A check and some photos were e______ed with the letter to the manager.

________ 5. Different cultures may cause m______g among people.

II. 字彙配合 (請忽略大小寫) (40%)

(A) broom (B) technician (C) nationality (D) publicity (E) freshman

_____ 1. It took some time for the _____ to adjust to her college life.

_____ 2. The _____ is the flying tool of the witch in this movie.

_____ 3. John has worked as a laboratory _____ for fifteen years.

_____ 4. Your _____ tells people what country you belong to.

_____ 5. The celebrity wanted to get married secretly and tried very hard to avoid _____.

III. 選擇題 (20%)

_____ 1. Anyone who _____ the civil law will face heavy fines in this city.
(A) violates (B) sketches (C) peddles (D) curves

_____ 2. There are too many errors of _____ in Mandy's composition.
(A) congratulation (B) appointment (C) grammar (D) intuition

_____ 3. The fans are all very excited that the third volume of the artist's autobiography is finally _____.
(A) stemmed (B) appointed (C) hawked (D) published

_____ 4. Everyone _____ Bill on winning the election yesterday.
(A) sketched (B) congratulated (C) curved (D) flouted

_____ 5. The _____ consisted of thirty people who concerned about animal welfare.
(A) assembly (B) stem (C) publicity (D) liar

Level 4 Test 23

Class: ________ No.: ________ Name: ________ Score: ________

I. 文意字彙 (40%)

______ 1. The company won the contract by using effective strategies to n______e with the client.

______ 2. Mr. Robinson will give l______es on modern poetry at the university this semester.

______ 3. A large number of people from Asia have i______ed to the United States in recent years.

______ 4. The driver was in v______n of the traffic regulations and was fined heavily.

______ 5. You'd better quit smoking because it would e______r your health.

II. 字彙配合 (請忽略大小寫) (40%)

(A) aquarium (B) bulletin (C) lifeguard (D) radar (E) skyscraper

______ 1. People can find a variety of fishes and sea creatures in the ______.

______ 2. The teacher pinned a list of class rules on the ______ board.

______ 3. The ______ looks odd and doesn't fit in with the surrounding buildings in the area.

______ 4. The ______ was praised for rescuing the drowning girl in the pool.

______ 5. When the airplane disappeared from the ______ screen, they knew something terrible had happened.

III. 選擇題 (20%)

______ 1. The maid wiped off the dirt with a ______ cloth.
(A) tense (B) grammatical (C) delightful (D) damp

______ 2. Two ______ were sent to rescue the hikers trapped in the canyon.
(A) bulletins (B) scolds (C) helicopters (D) quilts

______ 3. You must ______ your fear of speaking in front of people if you want to be a host.
(A) conquer (B) frost (C) strive (D) damp

______ 4. Audrey tasted all kinds of ______ and pizza when traveling in Italy.
(A) damp (B) pasta (C) tense (D) frost

______ 5. The manager ______ Katherine the new job.
(A) clarified (B) assigned (C) entertained (D) scolded

Level 4

Level 4 Test 24

Class: ________ No.: ________ Name: ________ Score: ________

I. 文意字彙 (40%)

______ 1. The teachers had a d______n against the new educational policy on Teachers' Day.

______ 2. The government will e______e tougher laws so that the traffic will improve.

______ 3. The young girl likes to wear bright red l______k.

______ 4. The b______r slid out of the house when no one was noticing.

______ 5. Why did the woman f______n at you? Did you do anything wrong?

II. 字彙配合 (請忽略大小寫) (40%)

(A) stroked (B) raisins (C) tickled (D) settlers (E) assured

______ 1. Nancy ______ the cat lovingly as it lay in her lap.

______ 2. The doctor ______ his patient that he would recover from the illness within a month.

______ 3. The little girl got ______ and couldn't stop giggling.

______ 4. Some kids love to eat ______, which are made of grapes dried in the sun.

______ 5. Most early ______ in America were from England and other European countries.

III. 選擇題 (20%)

______ 1. Cartoonists always work under pressure to meet the ______.
(A) spear (B) deadline (C) cliff (D) raisin

______ 2. We rent the mountaineering ______ before heading off.
(A) assurance (B) immigration (C) equipment (D) tickle

______ 3. The new shopping mall is a ______ of activity.
(A) graph (B) hive (C) lecturer (D) rage

______ 4. Isla ______ a piece of meat with her fork and put it into her mouth.
(A) raged (B) speared (C) pawed (D) assured

______ 5. Elio's trip to Rome turned into a ______ after his passport was stolen.
(A) nightmare (B) stroke (C) mule (D) paw

Level 4 Test 25

Class: ________ No.: ________ Name: ________ Score: ________

I. 文意字彙 (40%)

________ 1. The old man felt so depressed about his illness that he finally c______ted suicide.

________ 2. Elle's skirt was too short, so the teacher asked her to l______n it.

________ 3. If a n______r war breaks out, the whole world will be destroyed.

________ 4. The baby looked at his own r______n in the mirror and then laughed out loud.

________ 5. Tim is too old to make a living and has to be on w______e.

II. 字彙配合 (請忽略大小寫) (40%)

(A) furnished (B) decoration (C) liquor (D) determination (E) sewed

_____ 1. The department store has changed its _____ to greet the coming of Christmas.

_____ 2. Gary went to a _____ store and bought a bottle of whiskey before he went home.

_____ 3. The room for rent is _____ with a desk, a chair, a sofa bed, and a wardrobe.

_____ 4. The button of the coat came off, so Ruby _____ it back on the coat.

_____ 5. Mindy's _____ to win the contest drives her to practice day and night.

III. 選擇題 (20%)

_____ 1. Austin _____ his wife for verbally abusing him last month.
(A) sewed (B) sued (C) autographed (D) shortened

_____ 2. After a series of brutal killings, the police are trying to find out who the mass _____ is.
(A) atom (B) sewing (C) homeland (D) murderer

_____ 3. Violet _____ the picture she liked best and hung it on the wall.
(A) peeped (B) imposed (C) sewed (D) enlarged

_____ 4. There will be a _____ after the awards ceremony.
(A) timetable (B) reception (C) peep (D) cane

_____ 5. After the death of the artist, her _____ became extremely valuable.
(A) autograph (B) constitution (C) enlargement (D) gratitude

Level 4 Test 26

Class: ________ No.: ________ Name: ________ Score: ________

I. 文意字彙 (40%)

________ 1. We should choose proper r______n to help us relieve pressure and refresh our energy.

________ 2. So far, only fifteen people have r______red for the workshop.

________ 3. The eloquent speaker made a good i______n on the audience.

________ 4. The government offers l______ns to the students who need financial assistance.

________ 5. The old woman lives alone, and the cat becomes her closest c______n.

II. 字彙配合 (請忽略大小寫) (40%)

(A) honeymoon	(B) librarian	(C) timid	(D) shade	(E) stingy

_____ 1. If you cannot find a book in the library, you can ask a _____ to help you.

_____ 2. Simon is very _____ with money. He even doesn't want to spend much money on his children.

_____ 3. My grandmother likes to sit in the _____ of the large oak tree in hot summer days.

_____ 4. Be brave. Don't be as _____ as a rabbit.

_____ 5. The newlyweds went to Paris on their _____.

III. 選擇題 (20%)

_____ 1. The train will _____ for Kaohsiung from Taipei in ten minutes.
(A) telegraph (B) depart (C) exaggerate (D) obtain

_____ 2. My aunt's backyard is _____ with the smell of roses.
(A) gazed (B) enrolled (C) perfumed (D) bargained

_____ 3. Claire's grandfather has been buried in the _____.
(A) grave (B) capitalist (C) explanation (D) withdrawal

_____ 4. Two _____ bombs were dropped on Hiroshima and Nagasaki in 1945.
(A) stingy (B) atomic (C) shy (D) confident

_____ 5. Iris works as a design _____ for a home remodeling company.
(A) murmur (B) fragrance (C) bargain (D) consultant

Level 4 Test 27

Class: ________ No.: ________ Name: ________ Score: ________

I. 文意字彙 (40%)

________ 1. The i____d were sent to the hospital immediately.

________ 2. Helping others is a n____e deed.

________ 3. The company needs an a____t to examine their financial accounts.

________ 4. It is comfortable to have a picnic under the s____y trees.

________ 5. Mom will get mad if you wipe your g____y hands on the sofa.

II. 字彙配合 (請忽略大小寫) (40%)

(A) catalogue (B) tension (C) recycle (D) lobster (E) extend

____ 1. John and his girlfriend had ____ at a very expensive seafood restaurant, which cost them a fortune.

____ 2. As there are so many interesting things to do and see in Paris, we have decided to ____ our stay there.

____ 3. The best way to ease ____ is to do something you are interested in.

____ 4. If we ____ as much as possible, we will decrease the amount of garbage.

____ 5. Please mail me a(n) ____ of your company's products.

III. 選擇題 (20%)

____ 1. There are severe ____ on the use of guns in that country.
(A) barriers (B) stockings (C) philosophers (D) limitations

____ 2. Doris changed her NT dollars for euros before her ____ for Greece.
(A) restriction (B) departure (C) registration (D) horizon

____ 3. Noah was completely ____ after completing a long marathon training.
(A) tolerant (B) sporadic (C) continual (D) exhausted

____ 4. The training course is ____ to anyone over the age of eighteen.
(A) geared (B) composed (C) attached (D) recycled

____ 5. The scientific report was ____ by Canadian researchers and professionals.
(A) catalogued (B) exhausted (C) harmed (D) consisted

Level 4

Level 4 Test 28

Class: ________ No.: ________ Name: ________ Score: ________

I. 文意字彙 (40%)

________ 1. My brother made a s______n that we should go on a picnic.

________ 2. The skilled mechanic carried out a thorough i______n of my old car.

________ 3. Peter was talking n______e so we paid no attention to what he said.

________ 4. The space shuttle is now in o______t around the moon.

________ 5. One of the most amazing items found in the king's t______b was the magnificent golden mask.

II. 字彙配合 (請忽略大小寫) (40%)

(A) terror	(B) faithful	(C) horrifying	(D) linen	(E) blade

_____ 1. Tim was cut by his razor _____ while shaving this morning.

_____ 2. Chris was not _____ to his wife. He had cheated on her three times.

_____ 3. The dining table is covered with a white _____ tablecloth.

_____ 4. Rose was frightened to see the _____ scene.

_____ 5. While seeing something strange outside her window, Jenny screamed in _____.

III. 選擇題 (20%)

_____ 1. Sam showed great _____ in learning a second language.
(A) expansion (B) diligence (C) chemistry (D) rubbish

_____ 2. These early booking tickets are not _____ before the end of this month.
(A) copper (B) horrified (C) loyal (D) refundable

_____ 3. The laws that _____ the use of AI technology in the workplace have been under discussion recently.
(A) appall (B) grind (C) accuse (D) regulate

_____ 4. Ms. Wu prefers to use _____ aids in teaching English to her students.
(A) faithful (B) audiovisual (C) horrific (D) loyal

_____ 5. Nathan had a quick _____ before going for an interview.
(A) shave (B) grave (C) composer (D) germ

Level 4 Test 29

Class: ________ No.: ________ Name: ________ Score: ________

I. 文意字彙 (40%)

________ 1. When Mary turned down his invitation to dinner, John had a feeling of r_____n.

________ 2. Losing my job is a b_____g in disguise because I have more time with my children now.

________ 3. Jim is just a casual a_____e in business. I don't know him well.

________ 4. Henry has a f_____y of becoming the president of the country.

________ 5. The parliament was under the s_____y of the demanding king.

II. 字彙配合 (請忽略大小寫) (40%)

(A) insulted (B) farewell (C) nursery (D) orchestra (E) cherished

_____ 1. Olivia's dream of playing the trumpet in the _____ finally came true.

_____ 2. Philip _____ me by teasing about my weight in front of so many people.

_____ 3. We held a(n) _____ party in honor of the sales manager, who is going to retire next week.

_____ 4. Alex _____ the old watch that his grandfather gave him for his birthday.

_____ 5. I work in a(n) _____ and take care of the children.

III. 選擇題 (20%)

_____ 1. Being a(n) _____ mother at home and a dedicated supervisor at work simultaneously is not easy.
(A) enormous (B) measurable (C) devoted (D) gigantic

_____ 2. The truck suddenly came to a _____ in the middle of the highway.
(A) pickle (B) hose (C) halt (D) cord

_____ 3. We have to be trained to operate the machines safely under safety _____.
(A) regulations (B) autobiographies (C) diplomats (D) insults

_____ 4. It was a pity that Eva didn't have much time for _____ when she went to India on business.
(A) acceptance (B) sightseeing (C) translation (D) logic

_____ 5. Zack tried to _____ the song from Japanese into Chinese.
(A) devote (B) treasure (C) wave (D) translate

Level 4 Test 30

Class: ________ No.: ________ Name: ________ Score: ________

I. 文意字彙 (40%)

________ 1. I am a_____ting your reply. Please call me back as soon as possible.

________ 2. We stayed in a c_____e rather than a hotel while traveling in the small town.

________ 3. Sue couldn't help b_____king her eyes when she saw a flash of strong light ahead.

________ 4. In a p_____l discussion, several people are giving their opinions on a certain issue.

________ 5. I couldn't stop g_____ling upon seeing Leo's funny facial expression.

II. 字彙配合 (請忽略大小寫) (40%)

(A) relaxation	(B) logical	(C) sincerity	(D) housework	(E) fatal

_____ 1. If you cannot give a _____ explanation, nobody will accept your theory.

_____ 2. After a tiring day at work, Allen took a hot bath for _____.

_____ 3. Scientists are working hard to find a cure for the _____ disease.

_____ 4. I can say in all _____ that your cooking is the best.

_____ 5. Anita spent the weekend doing _____ so the house became clean.

III. 選擇題 (20%)

_____ 1. Ozzy is applying for a loan and hopes for a(n) _____ reply.
(A) favorable (B) addictive (C) congressional (D) illogical

_____ 2. The jazz singer _____ his fans with his drugs scandals.
(A) pioneered (B) chewed (C) disappointed (D) diagramed

_____ 3. Unfortunately, Frank took a(n) _____ and broke his left leg.
(A) tumble (B) translator (C) addict (D) chew

_____ 4. Shanice's car broke down, so she will have a car _____ fix it next Monday.
(A) diagram (B) mechanic (C) congress (D) trailblazer

_____ 5. You should adopt a _____ method that helps you work more efficiently.
(A) systematic (B) disappointing (C) nutritious (D) deadly

Level 4 Test 31

Class: ________ No.: ________ Name: ________ Score: ________

I. 文意字彙 (40%)

________ 1. The commercial is so impressive that almost everyone learns its s____n by heart.

________ 2. Andy was called a c____d by his friends because he was afraid of asking Lucy out.

________ 3. Bruce has been losing his hair recently. He is afraid he will go b____d soon.

________ 4. I didn't know how to deal with the t____e situation and turned to my father for advice.

________ 5. This book is written especially for students at the i____e level, not for beginners.

II. 文意選填 (請忽略大小寫) (40%)

(A) allowance (B) plentiful (C) ginger (D) perfection (E) memorable

____ 1. Two slices of ____ give the fish soup better flavor.

____ 2. Elsa spent most of her ____ on comic books.

____ 3. Every year, the rainy season will bring a(n) ____ supply of water.

____ 4. It was a(n) ____ experience to see a live performance from a world-famous singer.

____ 5. Sam's performance achieved ____. All the audience loved it every much.

III. 選擇題 (20%)

____ 1. The ____ development in the past decade has changed the way we work.
(A) annoying (B) technological (C) unforgettable (D) demoralized

____ 2. At times of ____, Lillian turns to nature for comfort.
(A) humidity (B) allowance (C) discouragement (D) perfection

____ 3. Lawyers and doctors ____ about forty percent of the committee.
(A) constitute (B) choke (C) slacken (D) fax

____ 4. Henry's boss hurt his feelings by making rude ____.
(A) diplomas (B) remarks (C) chokes (D) vegetarians

____ 5. When the flowers ____, Jasmine's garden is filled with fragrance.
(A) loosen (B) hasten (C) ferry (D) blossom

Level 4

Level 4 Test 32

Class: ______ No.: ______ Name: ______ Score: ______

I. 文意字彙 (40%)

______ 1. If you m____e an English word, you learn it by heart.

______ 2. Everyone admired the general for his l____y to his country.

______ 3. Kevin looked up at the stars in the sky through a t____e.

______ 4. Stacy danced gracefully because she had taken some b____t lessons in her childhood.

______ 5. Aside from f____ting on roast turkey, we also drank a lot of wine on Thanksgiving Day.

II. 文意選填 (請忽略大小寫) (40%)

(A) convenience	(B) interruption	(C) vital	(D) twig	(E) respectful

_____ 1. Annie picked the tender leaves from a(n) _____ of the tree.

_____ 2. Most _____ stores are open twenty-four hours in my city.

_____ 3. Students should be _____ to their teachers, even after graduation.

_____ 4. The politician made a speech for two hours without _____.

_____ 5. We can keep our _____ organs like the heart and brain healthy by exercising regularly.

III. 選擇題 (20%)

_____ 1. Jayden was grateful that his grandmother _____ his education.
(A) crept (B) financed (C) bounced (D) circulated

_____ 2. These soldiers are taught to be _____ to their general.
(A) ambiguous (B) glorious (C) obedient (D) divine

_____ 3. It took a lot of _____ to make Milo change his mind about telling me the truth.
(A) persuasion (B) interruption (C) disadvantage (D) repetition

_____ 4. Quinn was warned about the danger of putting fingers into electric _____.
(A) advantages (B) sockets (C) branches (D) plums

_____ 5. Look! A _____ of cattle is eating grass there.
(A) herd (B) bounce (C) banquet (D) hurricane

Level 4 Test 33

Class: ________ No.: ________ Name: ________ Score: ________

I. 文意字彙 (40%)

________ 1. Jack wrapped a b____e around his injured finger.

________ 2. Sam c____sed with his teacher about his goal in life.

________ 3. Jenny was d____d with the dirty dishes on the kitchen table. She hated washing dishes.

________ 4. Sandy was born in a rich family and has led a life of l____y since her birth.

________ 5. You may encounter all kinds of o____es while you are struggling for success. Don't feel discouraged.

II. 文意選填 (請忽略大小寫) (40%)

(A) hush	(B) isolated	(C) plumber	(D) ambitious	(E) gown

____ 1. Emma went to the party in an evening ____ yesterday.

____ 2. A(n) ____ fell over the auditorium when the speaker stood on the stage.

____ 3. Abby felt ____ at her new school. She didn't have any friends there.

____ 4. When the water pipe in the kitchen burst, Pauline called a(n) ____ to fix it.

____ 5. Tim is such a(n) ____ business person that he has opened ten chain stores within a year.

III. 選擇題 (20%)

____ 1. The firefighters ____ the injured workers from the burning factory.
(A) voyaged (B) calculated (C) restored (D) rescued

____ 2. Most ____ farmland, which produces the majority of crops, is located in the west of the island.
(A) useless (B) thorough (C) ambitious (D) fertile

____ 3. Doreen asked the judge to have ____ on her son.
(A) pesticide (B) extravagance (C) mercy (D) dislike

____ 4. The detective novel was highly praised by the literary ____.
(A) pests (B) critics (C) robes (D) hooks

____ 5. Luckily, Isabella ____ a big tuna within thirty minutes.
(A) hooked (B) fled (C) divorced (D) restored

Level 4 Test 34

Class: ________ No.: ________ Name: ________ Score: ________

I. 文意字彙 (40%)

________ 1. The father made faces to a____e his baby.

________ 2. Tired of city life, the couple r____ed to move to the countryside after retirement.

________ 3. The book with many color i____ns is suitable for children.

________ 4. It is t____l of Jane to remember my birthday and send me a gift.

________ 5. Irene has been c____ding with her high school classmates since graduation.

II. 文意選填 (請忽略大小寫) (40%)

(A) virtue (B) physician (C) dodge (D) sprinkle (E) disturb

____ 1. Would you like to ____ your soup with some pepper?

____ 2. John expected his child to go to medical school and become a ____.

____ 3. The children were taught the ____ of honesty through fairy tales and fables.

____ 4. Once we enter the library, we will stop talking in order not to ____ others.

____ 5. The mayor tried hard to ____ the embarrassing question about his affair with his secretary.

III. 選擇題 (20%)

____ 1. The ____ to the car accident made a statement about what had happened.

(A) basins (B) witnesses (C) sprinklers (D) crunches

____ 2. The comic books on the shelves are ____ according to authors.

(A) settled (B) offended (C) classified (D) evaded

____ 3. Kimberly broke her brother's toy car on purpose out of ____.

(A) jealousy (B) calculation (C) hydrogen (D) retirement

____ 4. The man bitten by a ____ spider on the right foot was sent to the hospital.

(A) mechanical (B) crunchy (C) graceful (D) poisonous

____ 5. Stella has a talent for language. She speaks ____ Italian and German.

(A) fluent (B) retired (C) considerate (D) fierce

Level 4 Test 35

Class: __________ No.: __________ Name: __________ Score: __________

I. 文意字彙 (40%)

__________ 1. These children are eager to dress up for the Halloween c______e parade.

__________ 2. The boy tried to c______h the can with his bare hands but he didn't have enough strength.

__________ 3. I was f______e enough to have such a good traveling companion.

__________ 4. The reporter's question a______yed the pop singer, so she refused to answer it.

__________ 5. According to official s______cs, the divorce rate is rising and the birth rate is declining.

II. 文意選填 (請忽略大小寫) (40%)

(A) draft (B) respectable (C) messy (D) offensive (E) merchant

_____ 1. Brian is tidying up his _____ room right now.

_____ 2. The dishonest _____ often cheats his customers by selling them fakes.

_____ 3. Ted showed me the first _____ of his novel and asked me to give him some suggestions.

_____ 4. The brave firefighter, who had rescued three people in the fire, was highly _____.

_____ 5. The gesture "thumbs up" is considered rude and _____ in some countries.

III. 選擇題 (20%)

_____ 1. In order to lose weight, Eliza counts _____ before eating.
(A) calories (B) revolutionaries (C) kettles (D) claws

_____ 2. Since Andrew is greatly interested in science, he will major in _____ at college.
(A) prediction (B) physics (C) identification (D) tolerance

_____ 3. The experts made a _____ that the stock market will drop next week.
(A) workplace (B) beggar (C) fireplace (D) prediction

_____ 4. Athena likes to _____ her grandfather's accent to make her sisters laugh.
(A) dominate (B) waken (C) imitate (D) draft

_____ 5. The CEO was _____ enough to invite me to his birthday party.
(A) revolutionary (B) claw (C) gracious (D) irritating

Level 4 Test 36

Class: ________ No.: ________ Name: ________ Score: ________

I. 文意字彙 (40%)

________ 1. Tim stopped rowing and let the boat d____t in the river.

________ 2. Patricia added two sugar c____es to make her coffee sweeter.

________ 3. The two business people exchanged g____gs and business cards before discussing the contract.

________ 4. You have to pay extra p____e if you want to send the letter by express.

________ 5. Twenty years after graduation, we are looking forward to the class r____n next week.

II. 文意選填 (請忽略大小寫) (40%)

(A) counter	(B) accompany	(C) dread	(D) tolerate	(E) millionaire

____ 1. How can you ____ such an irritating person?

____ 2. The criminal bribed the police under the ____.

____ 3. Tony made a fortune in the stock market and became a(n) ____.

____ 4. Many parents ____ their children on their first day of school.

____ 5. The thought of growing old without children around filled the mother with ____.

III. 選擇題 (20%)

____ 1. Naomi's repeated absences from school ____ that she didn't like school.
(A) blinked (B) dreaded (C) flattered (D) implied

____ 2. Howard was one of the leading ____ for the head coach.
(A) romances (B) counters (C) candidates (D) stereos

____ 3. It ____ Melissa that her application to the university was rejected.
(A) winked (B) knelt (C) frustrated (D) stood

____ 4. To my great surprise, this company employs their employees with regard to their religious ____.
(A) idiom (B) orientation (C) flattery (D) pregnancy

____ 5. The clerk made a sincere ____ to me for the long wait.
(A) stereo (B) apology (C) microscope (D) bin

Level 4 Test 37

Class: ________ No.: ________ Name: ________ Score: ________

I. 文意字彙 (40%)

________ 1. Don't i_____e your time away. Use it wisely.

________ 2. There are many outdoor f_____a markets in the city.

________ 3. Sarah never c_____es nagging her son to study harder, but he never listens.

________ 4. The dancer cried in f_____n after she knew she had lost the important competition.

________ 5. Not until I fell ill did I realize that it was not worthwhile to s_____e health for wealth.

II. 文意選填 (請忽略大小寫) (40%)

(A) torture	(B) biography	(C) lag	(D) pregnant	(E) drowsy

_____ 1. I feel _____ after having a glass of red wine.

_____ 2. The prisoner was forced to confess under _____.

_____ 3. A famous writer wrote a _____ of this brave soldier.

_____ 4. It took me two days to overcome jet _____ and feel energetic again.

_____ 5. You should make sure you are ready for motherhood before you get _____.

III. 選擇題 (20%)

_____ 1. Over one thousand _____ participated in the marathon event.
(A) tortures (B) presentations (C) stripes (D) competitors

_____ 2. Kai is a boy of _____, and thus he is very popular in the class.
(A) wit (B) revenge (C) indication (D) biography

_____ 3. The conductor _____ the band with a nod of her head.
(A) cued (B) lagged (C) milled (D) orphaned

_____ 4. Lucy is giving a _____ on the product she is promoting.
(A) mill (B) presentation (C) ministry (D) grief

_____ 5. Logan's contribution to this town was _____.
(A) striped (B) dusty (C) admirable (D) sleepy

Level 4 Test 38

Class: ________ No.: ________ Name: ________ Score: ________

I. 文意字彙 (40%)

________ 1. Can you s_____e your report in several sentences?

________ 2. Candice decided to s_____e the opportunity to study abroad.

________ 3. Molly's cat a_____hes its back and lifts its tail when it gets angry.

________ 4. Thomas was scolded for not f_____hing the toilet after using it.

________ 5. The appearance of Joan's ex-husband c_____ed her marriage.

II. 文意選填 (請忽略大小寫) (40%)

(A) tremendous (B) cunning (C) miner (D) mischief (E) economical

_____ 1. Jessie's father used to be a(n) _____ and worked underground all day.

_____ 2. Penny thanked her husband for the _____ support he had given her.

_____ 3. Nicole is worried about her son because he always gets into _____.

_____ 4. Mary is _____ with her money. She thinks twice before she buys anything.

_____ 5. Timothy is such a(n) _____ person that you should be very careful when doing business with him.

III. 選擇題 (20%)

_____ 1. Mary decided to _____ her hair purple, which made her mother angry.
(A) blush (B) grab (C) bloom (D) dye

_____ 2. In this fairy tale, the _____ turned the prince into a frog.
(A) arch (B) chamber (C) oval (D) witch

_____ 3. When the president died, many politicians attended his _____.
(A) funeral (B) admiration (C) politeness (D) revision

_____ 4. The local government is in charge of the _____ of the historic site.
(A) courtesy (B) preservation (C) priority (D) inflation

_____ 5. The Eiffel Tower is one of France's most famous _____.
(A) chambers (B) landmarks (C) guardians (D) idols

Level 4 Test 39

Class: ________ No.: ________ Name: ________ Score: ________

I. 文意字彙 (40%)

________ 1. Who is that little girl with beautiful blond c____ls?

________ 2. An enthusiastic person is usually highly m____ed to achieve his or her goal.

________ 3. Tina protested her i____e. She kept saying that she didn't steal Sandy's ring.

________ 4. You should replace the word "fury" with "rage" if you want it to r____e with "cage."

________ 5. Despite protests from the locals, the construction of the factory is still p____ding.

II. 文意選填 (請忽略大小寫) (40%)

(A) overcoat (B) surgeon (C) agreeable (D) ignorant (E) pronunciation

____ 1. The ____ is going to perform an operation on the patient.

____ 2. The boy is so ____ about cooking that he can't even fry an egg.

____ 3. It was cold outside, so Lily put on her ____ and turned up the collar.

____ 4. I have to check the dictionary to make sure of the ____ of the word.

____ 5. The two companies were ____ to the proposal and tried to draw up a contract.

III. 選擇題 (20%)

____ 1. The cruel way the man treated the stray cat was ____.
(A) elegant (B) gifted (C) shameful (D) mineral

____ 2. Though Ryan is on a diet, he cannot stand the ____ to have some sweets.
(A) workout (B) urge (C) foam (D) crack

____ 3. Sandra finally won the ____, which she had been dreaming about for years.
(A) boast (B) championship (C) mineral (D) guilt

____ 4. The little boy asked the ____ for help when he failed to get off the train at the right station.
(A) overcoat (B) elegance (C) earphone (D) conductor

____ 5. Jamie and Irene always have a ____ in the gym after work.
(A) surgeon (B) workout (C) championship (D) crack

Level 4 Test 40

Class: ________ No.: ________ Name: ________ Score: ________

I. 文意字彙 (40%)

________ 1. All passengers are f______n to smoke on the plane.

________ 2. The baby kept y______ning until he completely fell asleep.

________ 3. Linda does not dare to go p______ting. She is afraid of height.

________ 4. It was a great m______e that Henry lost his wallet during his trip to Italy.

________ 5. The police officer finally c______sed that he had been involved in the bribery.

II. 文意選填 (請忽略大小寫) (40%)

(A) riddle (B) lean (C) input (D) amateur (E) bracelet

_____ 1. Lisa always wears a silver _____ at work.

_____ 2. The event remained a(n) _____ in history. It probably can never be solved.

_____ 3. Shelly is so skillful at playing golf that nobody can tell she is a(n) _____.

_____ 4. You should make your own living and not _____ on your parents for financial help.

_____ 5. We have to _____ all the names, addresses, phone numbers and other personal data of our staff into the computer to have personnel files.

III. 選擇題 (20%)

_____ 1. Vanessa is on the day _____ in the emergency room.
(A) characteristic (B) shift (C) output (D) mystery

_____ 2. The _____ of plane was never found after the air crash.
(A) wreck (B) usage (C) aspirin (D) economist

_____ 3. The _____ area is suitable for growing tea plants because of its humid climate.
(A) mountainous (B) professional (C) imaginary (D) youthful

_____ 4. To his _____, the sales manager forgot his client's name.
(A) prosperity (B) embarrassment (C) craft (D) hardware

_____ 5. The bank robbers were ordered to _____ their guns by the police.
(A) surrender (B) prosper (C) glimpse (D) shift

Level 5-1 Test 1

Class: ________ No.: ________ Name: ________ Score: ________

I. 文意字彙 (40%)

________ 1. The writer appeared at the press conference to b____t the sales of his new book.

________ 2. The water shortage was caused by the d____t.

________ 3. Even though the two diamond rings have different designs, they are e____t in value.

________ 4. The company has a good p____n plan for the retired employees.

________ 5. The car slowed down to let the ambulance o____e.

II. 字彙配合 (請忽略大小寫) (40%)

(A) volcano (B) sequence (C) intent (D) abuse (E) olive

____ 1. Students devote themselves to a campaign against the ____ of drugs among teenagers.

____ 2. The ____ of the media is to divert our attention away from the scandal.

____ 3. It is said that ____ oil can help prevent heart disease.

____ 4. After the dancer performed a(n) ____ of perfect dancing moves, the crowd applauded.

____ 5. The ____ erupted violently yesterday. We could see the lava flowing down the mountain into the sea.

III. 選擇題 (20%)

____ 1. Nelson decided to create some hidden drawers to get more ____ space.
(A) equation (B) intention (C) storage (D) sequence

____ 2. Dylan ____ away when he saw the manager coming.
(A) sneaked (B) insisted (C) sequenced (D) certificated

____ 3. Ten contestants are ____ for the prize in this cooking reality show.
(A) looping (B) incorporating (C) abusing (D) contending

____ 4. Although Monica is a(n) ____ in Taiwan, she can speak fluent Taiwanese.
(A) clause (B) alien (C) provision (D) skull

____ 5. Only a(n) ____ teacher is allowed to work in our school.
(A) excessive (B) theoretical (C) certificated (D) worthy

Level 5-1 Test 2

Class: ________ No.: ________ Name: ________ Score: ________

I. 文意字彙 (40%)

________ 1. The government has y________ded to the strike of the firefighters and agreed to raise their salary.

________ 2. A church is a place where people w________p God.

________ 3. All the personal details of the p________l are stored in the computer system.

________ 4. The town was left in c________s after the destructive typhoon.

________ 5. The internal affairs of a nation should be free from foreign i________e.

II. 字彙配合 (請忽略大小寫) (40%)

(A) errands (B) alliance (C) executive (D) shortage (E) ecologists

_____ 1. The little girl enjoys running _____ for her mother like buying things in the grocery store or picking up laundry from the cleaner's.

_____ 2. America formed a(n) _____ with the United Kingdom to fight against Iraq.

_____ 3. The _____ estimate that some species have been affected by nuclear leakage.

_____ 4. The heavy rain ended the _____ of water.

_____ 5. The top _____ knows that any wrong decision she makes could have serious consequences for the company.

III. 選擇題 (20%)

_____ 1. Caleb has a(n) _____ ability in music. He should take some piano lessons to develop his talent.
(A) marine (B) executive (C) exceptional (D) sober

_____ 2. The amusement park was closed on Monday for routine _____.
(A) compassion (B) maintenance (C) ecology (D) shortage

_____ 3. Some students held a demonstration against the policies on _____ emission.
(A) shortage (B) compassion (C) carbon (D) conviction

_____ 4. Annie and I haven't watched the Australian _____ of the show.
(A) errand (B) version (C) slap (D) marine

_____ 5. The little boy who _____ to the handrail is afraid of falling down the stairs.
(A) clings (B) acknowledges (C) infects (D) overturns

Level 5-1 Test 3

Class: ________ No.: ________ Name: ________ Score: ________

I. 文意字彙 (40%)

________ 1. The latest blockbuster made the unknown actor a c______y overnight.

________ 2. The family didn't report the k______ping to the police.

________ 3. Please e______e on your question. I need to know more before I answer it.

________ 4. The United Kingdom used to be a major c______l power in the world.

________ 5. Many parents have difficulty communicating with their a______t children.

II. 字彙配合 (請忽略大小寫) (40%)

(A) choir (B) abnormal (C) extraordinary (D) exotic (E) quest

____ 1. Environmental pollution results in ____ weather conditions.

____ 2. John was fascinated by the ____ flowers while traveling in the small tropical country.

____ 3. Nick impressed us with his ____ achievements in chemistry.

____ 4. The archaeological team set off in ____ of Roman remains.

____ 5. James enjoyed singing and joined a church ____.

III. 選擇題 (20%)

____ 1. The project leader has ____ jobs to her members.

(A) tolled (B) allocated (C) flipped (D) kidnaped

____ 2. The coastal highway is ____ with the beach.

(A) finite (B) eternal (C) incredible (D) parallel

____ 3. The clerk had a quick ____ through all the products on the shelf.

(A) browse (B) parallel (C) toll (D) choir

____ 4. We need a marketing manager to oversee and ____ the whole project.

(A) coordinate (B) abolish (C) abduct (D) plead

____ 5. After a long discussion, the government and local residents finally reached a ____ over the environmental issue.

(A) skeleton (B) medication (C) compromise (D) flip

Level 5-1 Test 4

Class: ________ No.: ________ Name: ________ Score: ________

I. 文意字彙 (40%)

________ 1. Check the i____r of a house personally before you buy or rent it.

________ 2. Don't try to c____l the fact that you betrayed our trade secret to our rivals.

________ 3. Ivy and her husband s____ked up the sun on the beach.

________ 4. The man feels really nervous this time because he is no longer a spectator but one of the p____ts in the game.

________ 5. Martin Luther King Jr. was a strong a____e of the idea that all men are created equal.

II. 字彙配合 (請忽略大小寫) (40%)

(A) confidential	(B) metaphor	(C) ceremony	(D) ragged	(E) spicy

____ 1. A rose is often a ____ for love.

____ 2. Kelly loves these jeans so much that she does not want to throw them away even though they are ____.

____ 3. It was said that the FBI kept all the documents about aliens ____.

____ 4. Brian likes to eat hot and ____ dishes with a lot of chili powder in them.

____ 5. The wedding ____ will be held in the local church this Saturday.

III. 選擇題 (20%)

____ 1. The mall has undergone ____ renovations after change in ownership.
(A) grim (B) graphic (C) metaphorical (D) extensive

____ 2. Ian screwed up the presentation because he left the ____ of his work in the taxi.
(A) termination (B) portfolio (C) ally (D) torment

____ 3. Over the years, the small local shop has ____ into a big supermarket.
(A) stimulated (B) tortured (C) allied (D) evolved

____ 4. Henry was dumped by his girlfriend because he was afraid to make a(n) ____ in their relationship.
(A) abortion (B) ceremony (C) commitment (D) circuit

____ 5. The woman was condemned for ____ her pets.
(A) tormenting (B) accommodating (C) allying (D) evolving

Level 5-1 Test 5

Class: ________ No.: ________ Name: ________ Score: ________

I. 文意字彙 (40%)

________ 1. The sofa can be c______ted into a single bed.

________ 2. A whale is a m______l; it is not a fish.

________ 3. It's no e______n to say that Ms. Lin is the best teacher I've ever met.

________ 4. During the election campaign, the problem of bribery r______red its ugly head again.

________ 5. What the politician wants is power. He is i______t to the public interest.

II. 字彙配合 (請忽略大小寫) (40%)

(A) transformation (B) acute (C) passionate (D) sophisticated (E) sponge

_____ 1. This love letter showed his strong and _____ love for her, and she finally accepted his proposal.

_____ 2. Linda was immediately sent to the nearest hospital owing to a(n) _____ abdominal pain.

_____ 3. My dad wetted a(n) _____ and washed his car with it.

_____ 4. This device is highly _____ and can be used in aircrafts to guide directions.

_____ 5. The family structure in modern society has undergone an obvious _____.

III. 選擇題 (20%)

_____ 1. Lena always expresses opinions with confidence; _____ she will be chosen to take part in the speech contest.
(A) hence (B) alongside (C) prematurely (D) passionately

_____ 2. A crowd of demonstrators were protesting against job _____.
(A) consent (B) discrimination (C) clarity (D) fondness

_____ 3. Rachel is working for a multinational _____ at the moment.
(A) corporation (B) series (C) strap (D) sponge

_____ 4. Ed was angry when the server responded to his questions in a(n) _____ manner.
(A) passionate (B) external (C) comparable (D) abrupt

_____ 5. It seemed that Jessica felt no _____ for her adopted children.
(A) transformation (B) affection (C) interpretation (D) consent

Level 5-1 Test 6

Class: ________ No.: ________ Name: ________ Score: ________

I. 文意字彙 (40%)

________ 1. Many p______ts couldn't make enough money from farming to pay for their living.

________ 2. A new flu e______c broke out and struck down hundreds of people in a few days.

________ 3. To be i______e to the flu, you can get a flu vaccine.

________ 4. In the show, the juggler m______ed three balls skillfully with his hands.

________ 5. People with bipolar disorder usually a______e between anxiety and depression.

II. 字彙配合 (請忽略大小寫) (40%)

(A) juvenile	(B) correspondent	(C) souvenir	(D) trauma	(E) subtle

_____ 1. When Ian mentioned his ex-girlfriend, there was a _____ change in his voice that one could barely notice.

_____ 2. I hope Tommy can get over the emotional _____ of losing his pet.

_____ 3. The election result was _____ with the poll.

_____ 4. Jane bought a teddy bear as a _____ of her trip to London.

_____ 5. A _____ is prohibited from smoking.

III. 選擇題 (20%)

_____ 1. Milan Cathedral is a representative sample of Gothic _____ in Italy.
(A) penetration (B) absurdity (C) architecture (D) mockery

_____ 2. Having a stage fright, Eudora _____ over her lines in the drama.
(A) compensated (B) stumbled (C) mocked (D) penetrated

_____ 3. Belinda applied to medical school on the _____ of her teacher.
(A) conservation (B) recommendation
(C) administration (D) prescription

_____ 4. The little boy was awakened by the _____ noise from the building work.
(A) penetrating (B) equivalent (C) sham (D) farming

_____ 5. According to labor laws, normal working hours for employees should not _____ eight hours per day.
(A) mock (B) facilitate (C) copyright (D) exceed

Level 5-1 Test 7

Class: ________ No.: ________ Name: ________ Score: ________

I. 文意字彙 (40%)

________ 1. The c________ties of the tax laws confused a lot of taxpayers.

________ 2. Cynthia is an experienced s________t in breast cancer.

________ 3. Annie p________ed that the person behind her tried to steal her purse.

________ 4. Because of extreme physical f________e, Nelson died at the age of thirty.

________ 5. If you don't drink coffee, you can s________e tea for it.

II. 字彙配合 (請忽略大小寫) (40%)

(A) ultimate	(B) considerate	(C) expedition	(D) acceleration	(E) monopoly

_____ 1. The _____ in the decline of the rain forest worries a lot of scientists.

_____ 2. The little boy dreamed of going on a(n) _____ to another planet.

_____ 3. The government used to have a(n) _____ on the sale of tobacco and alcohol.

_____ 4. The _____ aim of these changes is to expand the factory.

_____ 5. You have to be more _____ of others' feelings.

III. 選擇題 (20%)

_____ 1. All the staff in the hotel is very _____ to us. We'll definitely visit here again!
(A) courteous (B) inconsiderate (C) alcoholic (D) noticeable

_____ 2. Bears have a(n) _____ sense of smell that allows them to find food from a long distance.
(A) superb (B) innovative (C) descriptive (D) final

_____ 3. The welfare system has been reformed during Mrs. Wu's _____.
(A) perception (B) coffin (C) rehearsal (D) presidency

_____ 4. Edward can't eat crabs since he has a(n) _____ to seafood.
(A) expert (B) allergy (C) cuisine (D) heritage

_____ 5. The school cafeteria doesn't serve _____ beverages.
(A) descriptive (B) alcoholic (C) perceptive (D) thoughtful

Level 5-1 Test 8

Class: ________ No.: ________ Name: ________ Score: ________

I. 文意字彙 (40%)

________ 1. The painter was c____ned to paint the portrait of the princess.

________ 2. Put on your coat l____t you should catch a cold.

________ 3. The sly man planned a scheme to u____e the president's credibility.

________ 4. I have no particular p____e for drinks. All I want is something that can quench my thirst.

________ 5. The teacher was looking for a____ns for her students when she took them on a school trip to a neighboring town.

II. 字彙配合 (請忽略大小寫) (40%)

(A) indispensable	(B) allergic	(C) applause	(D) profile	(E) expertise

____ 1. The audience gave warm ____ to the school choir.

____ 2. The politician has been keeping a low ____ since his scandal was exposed to the public.

____ 3. We were amazed at Joe's ____ in electrical engineering.

____ 4. Jacob always keeps his house tidy because he is ____ to dust.

____ 5. Regular exercise and a balanced diet are ____ to a healthy life.

III. 選擇題 (20%)

____ 1. Our bakery's ____ is lemon tart.
(A) reminder (B) layer (C) format (D) specialty

____ 2. COVID-19 is a highly ____ disease. It can be spread from one person to another through the air.
(A) allergic (B) sufficient (C) contagious (D) dispensable

____ 3. To our great surprise, the milk we bought was expired on the day of ____.
(A) expertise (B) purchase (C) milestone (D) essence

____ 4. People suffering from cancer may undergo radiation ____ to destroy cancer cells.
(A) format (B) productivity (C) debris (D) therapy

____ 5. In spite of her illness, Shelly ____ in conducting her experiments.
(A) persists (B) profiles (C) purchases (D) layers

Level 5-1 Test 9

Class: ________ No.: ________ Name: ________ Score: ________

I. 文意字彙 (40%)

______ 1. The newlyweds bought some electrical a______es for their new house.

______ 2. Reluctantly, the children m______ted their unwillingness to leave the amusement park.

______ 3. With Jill's e______t instructions, Peter found his way to the museum easily.

______ 4. The workers went on strike to ask for d______t payments.

______ 5. There are some fine s______ns of fossils in the museum.

II. 字彙配合 (請忽略大小寫) (40%)

(A) genetically (B) analyst (C) miniature (D) radically (E) accord

______ 1. My father depends on this financial ______ to tell him how to invest.

______ 2. With one ______, the audience stood up and applauded.

______ 3. The experts warned of the potential danger of ______ modified foods.

______ 4. The novel is real life in ______.

______ 5. The company ______ altered its marketing strategies in order to win back the customers it had lost over the last three years.

III. 選擇題 (20%)

______ 1. Once the new cement plant is built, the ______ balance will be changed.
(A) controversial (B) ecological (C) genetic (D) strategic

______ 2. The nurse took Fabian's ______ and found it quite weak.
(A) pulse (B) likelihood (C) removal (D) vacuum

______ 3. The television series ______ Leah's interest in European history.
(A) throbbed (B) aroused (C) fouled (D) executed

______ 4. We signed a ______ against the construction of the new nuclear power plant.
(A) radical (B) commodity (C) tactic (D) petition

______ 5. Apple Inc. has created many ______ inventions such as the iPhone and the iPad.
(A) unprecedented (B) tactical (C) muscular (D) foul

Level 5-1 Test 10

Class: ________ No.: ________ Name: ________ Score: ________

I. 文意字彙 (40%)

________ 1. Many animals are on the verge of e______n because their habitats have been destroyed.

________ 2. After the terrorist attacks, the budget for national defense has been m______y increased.

________ 3. The book h______ts the influence of the international situation on the country's economy.

________ 4. Belle was diagnosed with a t______l illness last night.

________ 5. Mia m______fied her draft again and again to make it more complete.

II. 字彙配合 (請忽略大小寫) (40%)

(A) gathering	(B) overall	(C) verbal	(D) pyramid	(E) anonymous

_____ 1. The husband cannot stand his wife's torrent of _____ abuse.

_____ 2. Jeff's wife received a(n) _____ letter whose writer claimed to have an affair with Jeff.

_____ 3. Every family member will attend the family _____ this Friday.

_____ 4. Studies show that a student's social background may have an influence on his _____ academic performance.

_____ 5. Visiting the ancient _____ has been on Tracy's bucket lists for a long time.

III. 選擇題 (20%)

_____ 1. Luke's sudden_____ of love made me quite shocked.
(A) reservoir (B) declaration (C) ecosystem (D) accounting

_____ 2. The ceremony ended with a(n) _____ firework display.
(A) spectacular (B) regardless (C) anonymous (D) mainstream

_____ 3. My father checks news _____ on the Internet every morning.
(A) railings (B) gatherings (C) pitchers (D) updates

_____ 4. The plan of building a new factory has faced fierce _____ from environmentalists.
(A) adaptation (B) communism (C) opposition (D) asset

_____ 5. The boss asked me to stop beating around the bush and get to the _____ of the problem.
(A) overall (B) array (C) core (D) rail

Level 5-1 Test 11

Class: ________ No.: ________ Name: ________ Score: ________

I. 文意字彙 (40%)

______ 1. Many people stood up to pay t______e to the distinguished scholar.

______ 2. Would you like to invest in s______ks and shares to create more wealth?

______ 3. This is not the first time they have met. In fact, they are already a______ted with each other.

______ 4. Here's my company's telephone number, and my e______n is 600.

______ 5. Tension is m______ting as we are all waiting anxiously for the result of the test.

II. 字彙配合 (請忽略大小寫) (40%)

(A) vague (B) plea (C) wildlife (D) recital (E) hostile

______ 1. Sean will give a piano ______ in the concert hall next Saturday.

______ 2. Julie only has a ______ impression of her primary school teachers.

______ 3. People are appealing to the government to protect the ______ in the country.

______ 4. The candidate made a ______ to the public for votes.

______ 5. Belinda is ______ to the idea of increasing taxes. She doesn't think it will help solve the current economic problems.

III. 選擇題 (20%)

______ 1. People who fill in the ______ will have a chance to win a special prize.
(A) federation (B) texture (C) questionnaire (D) mansion

______ 2. The news reporter is giving live ______ of the presidential campaign.
(A) coverage (B) revenue (C) arrogance (D) athletics

______ 3. Cuba and China are ______ countries.
(A) communist (B) arrogant (C) federal (D) indistinct

______ 4. Children are all eagerly ______ their Christmas party tomorrow.
(A) ascending (B) anticipating (C) awing (D) generating

______ 5. In order to reduce the budget ______, the company is considering laying off senior employees.
(A) performer (B) communist (C) deficit (D) sponsor

Level 5-1 Test 12

Class: ________ No.: ________ Name: ________ Score: ________

I. 文意字彙 (40%)

________ 1. Jack made a p____e not to drink alcohol anymore.

________ 2. Don't throw away this old-looking wardrobe! It is a valuable a____e.

________ 3. The damage of the earthquake is a____sed at ten billion dollars.

________ 4. Lottery numbers are chosen at r____m, and people who hold tickets with the same numbers win the prizes.

________ 5. Ethan s____ned his back when he lifted weights at the gym.

II. 字彙配合 (請忽略大小寫) (40%)

(A) contemporary (B) prey (C) commute (D) depict (E) nasty

____ 1. It takes Julie one hour to ____ from her home to Taipei every day.

____ 2. The pianist prefers ____ music to classical music.

____ 3. These two novels ____ the country life in the 18th century.

____ 4. Doves and pigeons ____ on fruits and seeds.

____ 5. John is really a ____ man who is always shouting at others for no reason.

III. 選擇題 (20%)

____ 1. The school authorities have lifted the ____ on hairstyles.
(A) midst (B) genre (C) fabric (D) ban

____ 2. The thundery shower forced us to take ____ from the rain in the restaurant.
(A) acquisition (B) flexibility (C) reverse (D) refuge

____ 3. The couple decided to ____ around the Mediterranean to celebrate their wedding anniversary.
(A) cruise (B) commute (C) prohibit (D) howl

____ 4. The factory faced a severe fine after accidentally releasing ____ chemicals into the river.
(A) modern (B) mean (C) toxic (D) reverse

____ 5. The little girl bought some cotton candy from a street ____ at a fair.
(A) reversal (B) vendor (C) commitment (D) predator

Level 5-1 Test 13

Class: ________ No.: ________ Name: ________ Score: ________

I. 文意字彙 (40%)

________ 1. The l____e child claimed to have a share of his father's property.

________ 2. After consideration, the old couple took the p____e and went traveling around the world by themselves.

________ 3. The actress just g____ed at the host when he asked her a personal question.

________ 4. Most of Julian's ideas were d____ed from those of his classmates. They influenced the way he looked at things.

________ 5. The boss doesn't think the project is c____e with the company's long-term goals.

II. 字彙配合 (請忽略大小寫) (40%)

(A) residence	(B) beloved	(C) fiber	(D) abundant	(E) prior

____ 1. To stay healthy, Sammy eats food that is high in ____.

____ 2. The earthquake deprived Kevin of his ____ family.

____ 3. Sebastian and his wife took up ____ in the north of Mexico.

____ 4. You should give me ____ notice if you have to cancel the meeting.

____ 5. Salmon are ____ in the river when the spawning season comes.

III. 選擇題 (20%)

____ 1. The island became a ____ wasteland after the government dumped nuclear waste on it.

(A) suburban (B) barren (C) beloved (D) fluid

____ 2. When spring comes, these birds will ____ north to their breeding ground.

(A) migrate (B) legitimate (C) saint (D) mock

____ 3. Josh's most attractive personality ____ is his sense of humor.

(A) residency (B) trait (C) migration (D) neutral

____ 4. The fishing village has the low population ____.

(A) saint (B) roughage (C) aptitude (D) density

____ 5. Pauline always stays ____ when her parents fight with each other.

(A) scarce (B) ridiculous (C) neutral (D) previous

Level 5-1

Level 5-1 Test 14

Class: ________ No.: ________ Name: ________ Score: ________

I. 文意字彙 (40%)

________ 1. The s____y football player has big muscles and can run very fast.

________ 2. Emily believes in the s____n that the number 4 is an unfortunate number.

________ 3. You should b____e of the aggressive dog. It may bite you.

________ 4. It's a v____s cycle that Ken stays up late at night and always feels sleepy in class. He should try to go to bed early.

________ 5. Eric threw c____n to the winds and ran into the burning house to rescue his son.

II. 字彙配合 (請忽略大小寫) (40%)

(A) naive	(B) trigger	(C) norm	(D) destination	(E) destructive

____ 1. Double-income families are becoming the ____ in modern society.

____ 2. Meg thinks Okinawa is the best holiday ____ for its dramatic landscape.

____ 3. Some still hold the ____ thought that everything on the news is true.

____ 4. The robber didn't pull the ____. Instead, he put his gun down.

____ 5. Lack of trust is very ____ to a marriage.

III. 選擇題 (20%)

____ 1. Climate action has been one of the ____ popular issues around the world.
(A) poetically (B) naively (C) likewise (D) immensely

____ 2. I am writing on ____ of my boss to arrange the meeting with you.
(A) administrator (B) behalf (C) resort (D) arena

____ 3. Benson will not attend a military academy since he doesn't like its ____ disciplines.
(A) malicious (B) naive (C) rigid (D) poetic

____ 4. The purpose of ____ the new policy is to improve road safety.
(A) implementing (B) forging (C) resorting (D) sowing

____ 5. Our company is looking for those who have a high level of ____ in English.
(A) possession (B) alteration (C) competence (D) setting

Level 5-1 Test 15

Class: ________ No.: ________ Name: ________ Score: ________

I. 文意字彙 (40%)

________ 1. We should take p______ns against mudslides during the typhoon season.

________ 2. The incident must have occurred s______t to our departure because we didn't see anything.

________ 3. The fertilizer is made from organic c______ds and can make plants grow better.

________ 4. Don't d______e against the disabled. You should treat them fairly.

________ 5. Sara has been working on her report for a whole month, but it is still n______e near completed.

II. 字彙配合 (請忽略大小寫) (40%)

(A) ritual (B) gross (C) mint (D) vulnerable (E) adoration

_____ 1. Tim is very sensitive and _____ to criticism.

_____ 2. Many tourists are interested in this ancient _____ that is performed by local people.

_____ 3. It's common to see a drink decorated with a sprig of _____.

_____ 4. People need to pay a certain percentage of their _____ income as a tax to the government.

_____ 5. Olivia looked at her puppy with _____.

III. 選擇題 (20%)

_____ 1. Leo's successful strike was _____ to our team's victory.
(A) previous (B) straightforward (C) crucial (D) biological

_____ 2. We should not waste time on _____ matters. Just get to the point!
(A) trivial (B) adorable (C) constituent (D) wild

_____ 3. Mia gave her student a concert ticket as a(n) _____ to attend the workshop.
(A) incentive (B) diagnosis (C) articulation (D) beneficiary

_____ 4. Giant pandas and golden monkeys are _____ to China.
(A) riotous (B) biological (C) indigenous (D) articulate

_____ 5. The politician is always accompanied by her personal _____.
(A) components (B) bodyguards (C) offerings (D) rituals

Level 5-1 Test 16

Class: ________ No.: ________ Name: ________ Score: ________

I. 文意字彙 (40%)

________ 1. Many animals are on the verge of extinction because their h_____ts have been destroyed.

________ 2. Our society used to have strong p_____e against unmarried mothers.

________ 3. Are you an o_____t of the death penalty?

________ 4. Having no c_____n of how serious the problem was, Jacky did not attempt to solve it.

________ 5. Dylan chose the noodle bar because of its "air conditioned" sign outside, but he was hit by a b_____t of hot air as he stepped into it.

II. 字彙配合 (請忽略大小寫) (40%)

(A) index	(B) noticeable	(C) obligation	(D) bound	(E) dilemma

_____ 1. Check the _____ to see where you can find these technical terms in the book.

_____ 2. Being a good citizen, you should not avoid the _____ of paying taxes.

_____ 3. The smell of curry is immediately _____ when you walk into the restaurant.

_____ 4. My sister was caught in a(n) _____ of whether to study abroad or just to find a job here.

_____ 5. Wyatt knows his sister is _____ to get married one day.

III. 選擇題 (20%)

_____ 1. The board worried that the strike will have a(n) _____ effect on the company.
(A) cognitive (B) rival (C) compulsory (D) adverse

_____ 2. After checking Ivy's medical report, Dr. Lin suggested that she should _____ further examination.
(A) bid (B) bound (C) understand (D) undergo

_____ 3. Ruby went to the hair _____ and had her hair dyed brown.
(A) salon (B) transmission (C) infrastructure (D) transfer

_____ 4. There's an obvious _____ between the twins. One is an early bird, while the other is a night owl.
(A) adversary (B) distinction (C) dilemma (D) obligation

_____ 5. Ed got completely drunk and made a(n) _____ of himself at his wedding.
(A) ass (B) index (C) competitor (D) franchise

Level 5-1 Test 17

Class: ________ No.: ________ Name: ________ Score: ________

I. 文意字彙 (40%)

________ 1. The student gets frustrated when he c______ts himself far worse than expected.

________ 2. Olivia feels excited at the p______t of studying abroad.

________ 3. The environmental groups i______ed a water conservation program.

________ 4. Congress will i______e some new laws to regulate working hours.

________ 5. A pair of s______ls is a good choice in summer.

II. 字彙配合 (請忽略大小寫) (40%)

(A) breakthrough	(B) structural	(C) obscure	(D) agenda	(E) assault

_____ 1. The earthquake caused some _____ damage to the building.

_____ 2. A(n) _____ is a list of subjects that will be discussed at a meeting.

_____ 3. The invention of computers was really a big _____ in technology.

_____ 4. We were confused about Alan's _____ explanation.

_____ 5. The soldiers were charged with _____ on the innocent people.

III. 選擇題 (20%)

_____ 1. If anyone knows the _____ of the escaped prisoner, please call the police.
(A) agendas (B) confrontations (C) whereabouts (D) ventures

_____ 2. The thunder _____ so loudly that everyone was quite shocked.
(A) boomed (B) conformed (C) distracted (D) obscured

_____ 3. Peter scored ten points in the _____ stage of the game.
(A) obscure (B) horizontal (C) preliminary (D) structural

_____ 4. After some consideration, Cleo _____ for a steady job in Dubai.
(A) plotted (B) maintained (C) reduced (D) opted

_____ 5. We gradually learn to cherish what we have as natural resources _____.
(A) sustain (B) diminish (C) scheme (D) divert

Level 5-1 Test 18

Class: ________ No.: ________ Name: ________ Score: ________

I. 文意字彙 (40%)

________ 1. Rita d______ed into tears on hearing the tragic event.

________ 2. At the bottom of the food chain, microscopic o______ms degrade the organic wastes.

________ 3. Poor h______g conditions are the main reasons for the low rent of this house.

________ 4. Recent research has shown that over twenty percent of the students are being b______lied at school.

________ 5. The old computer system was complicated, w______s the new one is simple.

II. 字彙配合 (請忽略大小寫) (40%)

(A) dreadful	(B) bureau	(C) optional	(D) valid	(E) currency

_____ 1. Let's go to the information _____ to get some guidebooks.

_____ 2. My mom bought a voucher _____ for two months.

_____ 3. The opening ceremony has been postponed because of the _____ weather.

_____ 4. Although you can pay with a credit card, you'd better prepare some foreign _____ when traveling abroad.

_____ 5. This writing course is not a(n) _____ one, so every student has to take it.

III. 選擇題 (20%)

_____ 1. The man broke his legs in the crash and has been in a _____ ever since.
(A) segment (B) journalist (C) wheelchair (D) ratio

_____ 2. The French restaurant is widely praised for its _____ dishes.
(A) distinctive (B) submissive (C) valid (D) scandalous

_____ 3. Mike is promoted to senior director, and now there are fifty people under his _____.
(A) supervision (B) validity (C) scandal (D) insight

_____ 4. Joanne was so lucky that she just got a few _____ in the accident.
(A) claims (B) bruises (C) segments (D) bureaus

_____ 5. Mother Teresa's _____ to the poor and the sick is well-known.
(A) devotion (B) aggression (C) validity (D) currency

Level 5-1 Test 19

Class: ________ No.: ________ Name: ________ Score: ________

I. 文意字彙 (40%)

________ 1. Farmers are taught to use new methods to increase the o______t of their crops.

________ 2. Jack made a copy of the important d______t as a backup.

________ 3. We think the man is guilty. What's your s______t on this issue?

________ 4. The weather forecast says it will be p______y cloudy tomorrow.

________ 5. The motorcyclist was hit by a car and lying in a______y in the middle of the road.

II. 字彙配合 (請忽略大小寫) (40%)

(A) progressive	(B) widespread	(C) donation	(D) assumption	(E) theft

_____ 1. There is _____ concern that the new factory will make the pollution worse.

_____ 2. On the _____ that the economy will revive next year, Linda invests all her money in the stock market.

_____ 3. After the major redesign, the old village has become a _____ community.

_____ 4. Lisa makes a(n) _____ to the children in poor areas every month.

_____ 5. John was put into jail for car _____.

III. 選擇題 (20%)

_____ 1. The land was no longer appropriate for agriculture because of the groundwater _____.
(A) contamination (B) calcium (C) nutrition (D) variation

_____ 2. In some cases, minor injuries can become _____ if they are untreated.
(A) deadly (B) eloquent (C) sensational (D) witty

_____ 3. The bodies of the victims in the earthquake were sent home for _____.
(A) assumption (B) contamination (C) donation (D) burial

_____ 4. Ken and May held their wedding in an old _____.
(A) sensation (B) progressive (C) hypothesis (D) cathedral

_____ 5. Owen has a regular checkup to see if he has any _____ associated with cancer.
(A) burials (B) variations (C) syndromes (D) institutions

Level 5-1 Test 20

Class: ________ No.: ________ Name: ________ Score: ________

I. 文意字彙 (40%)

________ 1. The manager is the v____l head of the branch office in Taichung.

________ 2. Traditional handicrafts have been on the d____e. They have become less and less popular.

________ 3. The security guards on p____l stopped a man who was trying to sneak into the office building.

________ 4. Never buy anything on i____e. Think carefully before spending your money.

________ 5. Jenny suddenly cried when her mother held her in a warm e____e.

II. 字彙配合 (請忽略大小寫) (40%)

(A) astonished	(B) eligible	(C) chef	(D) aisle	(E) workshop

_____ 1. The dancer looked _____ when the result was announced.

_____ 2. Anyone over twenty is _____ for membership.

_____ 3. The clerk at the grocery store told me that olive oil was in _____ six.

_____ 4. Only the _____ knows the secret recipe for the traditional cuisine.

_____ 5. Miranda joined the drama _____ and found it was very helpful in improving her acting skills.

III. 選擇題 (20%)

_____ 1. In this song, the _____ harmonize with the background music perfectly.
(A) urges (B) lawsuits (C) vocals (D) sheds

_____ 2. Natalie is a natural leader. She has the _____ to motivate her team.
(A) capability (B) amazement (C) evolution (D) temptation

_____ 3. Jill and David _____ going on a trip to Fiji on their honeymoon.
(A) oversaw (B) contemplated (C) prolonged (D) shed

_____ 4. Fortunately, most plants in the yard remained _____ after the typhoon.
(A) rash (B) intact (C) eligible (D) cautious

_____ 5. In Taiwan, _____ elections are held every four years.
(A) presidential (B) prolonged (C) risky (D) impetuous

核心英文字彙力 2001～4500 習題本

Answer Key

Level 3 Test 1
I. 1. stomach 2. communicate 3. informed
4. vanished 5. patience
II. 1. B 2. D 3. E 4. C 5. A
III. 1. A 2. C 3. B 4. B 5. D

Level 3 Test 2
I. 1. buckets 2. situations 3. practical
4. intelligent 5. connected
II. 1. B 2. C 3. A 4. D 5. E
III. 1. D 2. B 3. C 4. A 5. D

Level 3 Test 3
I. 1. invented 2. warned 3. polluted
4. achieve 5. appealed
II. 1. D 2. B 3. E 4. A 5. C
III. 1. C 2. B 3. A 4. B 5. D

Level 3 Test 4
I. 1. representative 2. inventors
3. stripped 4. litter 5. techniques
II. 1. A 2. E 3. C 4. D 5. B
III. 1. B 2. D 3. D 4. B 5. A

Level 3 Test 5
I. 1. salary 2. responsibility 3. dishonest
4. benefited 5. admired
II. 1. B 2. C 3. A 4. E 5. D
III. 1. A 2. B 3. A 4. D 5. C

Level 3 Test 6
I. 1. aware 2. scary 3. significant
4. efficient 5. comfort
II. 1. B 2. C 3. A 4. E 5. D
III. 1. C 2. A 3. B 4. D 5. A

Level 3 Test 7
I. 1. capable 2. ambition 3. approve
4. remote 5. emotional
II. 1. D 2. B 3. C 4. A 5. E
III. 1. C 2. B 3. A 4. B 5. D

Level 3 Test 8
I. 1. complaints 2. revealed 3. competes
4. suffering 5. citizen
II. 1. E 2. D 3. B 4. A 5. C
III. 1. B 2. D 3. A 4. A 5. C

Level 3 Test 9
I. 1. tourism 2. talent 3. attitude
4. electricity 5. creatures
II. 1. D 2. B 3. E 4. C 5. A
III. 1. C 2. B 3. D 4. A 5. C

Level 3 Test 10
I. 1. advised 2. exhibition 3. threatened
4. clinic 5. audience
II. 1. C 2. B 3. E 4. D 5. A
III. 1. D 2. A 3. B 4. D 5. C

Level 3 Test 11
I. 1. political 2. wealthy 3. career
4. expectations 5. technical
II. 1. C 2. B 3. A 4. D 5. E
III. 1. B 2. C 3. A 4. A 5. B

Level 3 Test 12
I. 1. election 2. majority 3. experimented
4. territory 5. decreased
II. 1. D 2. B 3. C 4. E 5. A
III. 1. C 2. B 3. D 4. C 5. A

Level 3 Test 13
I. 1. beneath 2. awkward 3. impressed
4. Meanwhile 5. collection
II. 1. C 2. B 3. A 4. D 5. E
III. 1. C 2. A 3. A 4. D 5. C

Level 3 Test 14
I. 1. leather 2. moisture 3. excellence
4. operation 5. bound
II. 1. B 2. D 3. A 4. E 5. C
III. 1. A 2. D 3. A 4. D 5. A

Level 3 Test 15
I. 1. injury 2. handful 3. bacteria
4. substances 5. recognize
II. 1. A 2. C 3. E 4. B 5. D
III. 1. C 2. A 3. B 4. D 5. C

Level 3 Test 16
I. 1. vacant 2. nickname 3. observing
4. mental 5. bores
II. 1. E 2. D 3. C 4. A 5. B
III. 1. B 2. D 3. A 4. C 5. D

Level 3 Test 17

I. 1. exploring 2. preparations 3. indoors 4. hesitates 5. location

II. 1. B 2. E 3. C 4. D 5. A

III.1. B 2. B 3. A 4. B 5. D

Level 3 Test 18

I. 1. protection 2. property 3. capture 4. resources 5. tossed

II. 1. E 2. D 3. A 4. C 5. B

III.1. B 2. D 3. C 4. A 5. C

Level 3 Test 19

I. 1. vitamin 2. acceptable 3. reasonable 4. spite 5. statue

II. 1. C 2. B 3. A 4. D 5. E

III.1. B 2. C 3. A 4. D 5. C

Level 3 Test 20

I. 1. steady 2. bumped 3. breeze 4. reduce 5. traced

II. 1. B 2. E 3. D 4. C 5. A

III.1. A 2. A 3. B 4. C 5. A

Level 3 Test 21

I. 1. hopeful 2. stale 3. teenage 4. envy 5. float

II. 1. B 2. A 3. E 4. D 5. C

III.1. B 2. B 3. A 4. C 5. C

Level 3 Test 22

I. 1. horrible 2. fainted 3. temper 4. receipt 5. lately

II. 1. A 2. B 3. C 4. E 5. D

III.1. A 2. C 3. B 4. A 5. D

Level 3 Test 23

I. 1. bravery 2. grasp 3. horror 4. apologize 5. fountain

II. 1. C 2. E 3. D 4. B 5. A

III.1. B 2. C 3. B 4. A 5. C

Level 3 Test 24

I. 1. assisted 2. relief 3. humid 4. tent 5. froze

II. 1. A 2. C 3. E 4. D 5. B

III.1. D 2. D 3. D 4. B 5. A

Level 3 Test 25

I. 1. resist 2. knight 3. stormy 4. greenhouse 5. hungers

II. 1. C 2. D 3. A 4. E 5. B

III.1. B 2. A 3. D 4. A 5. B

Level 3 Test 26

I. 1. glance 2. thankful 3. Subtract 4. automobile 5. cigarettes

II. 1. C 2. D 3. E 4. B 5. A

III.1. D 2. A 3. C 4. D 5. A

Level 3 Test 27

I. 1. flames 2. licking 3. buffet 4. thirst 5. scarf

II. 1. B 2. E 3. A 4. D 5. C

III.1. B 2. A 3. B 4. B 5. D

Level 3 Test 28

I. 1. hourly 2. stiff 3. bulbs 4. mended 5. Rumor

II. 1. D 2. B 3. E 4. C 5. A

III.1. D 2. D 3. B 4. A 5. C

Level 3 Test 29

I. 1. baggage 2. locate 3. regret 4. satisfactory 5. laughter

II. 1. A 2. C 3. B 4. E 5. D

III.1. D 2. A 3. C 4. B 5. C

Level 3 Test 30

I. 1. innocent 2. politician 3. restrict 4. suspicion 5. wander

II. 1. B 2. A 3. D 4. E 5. C

III.1. A 2. B 3. A 4. D 5. B

Level 3 Test 31

I. 1. parade 2. jail 3. poll 4. swore 5. loose

II. 1. B 2. C 3. D 4. A 5. E

III.1. A 2. D 3. B 4. D 5. B

Level 3 Test 32

I. 1. weakened 2. sometime 3. roared 4. foggiest 5. separation

II. 1. D 2. C 3. E 4. B 5. A

III.1. B 2. D 3. B 4. A 5. C

Level 3 Test 33

I. 1. ache 2. handy 3. spice 4. sexual 5. jealous

II. 1. E 2. A 3. D 4. C 5. B

III.1. C 2. A 3. B 4. A 5. C

Level 3 Test 34

I. 1. coconut 2. inspected 3. mankind 4. sensible 5. beast

II. 1. C 2. A 3. B 4. E 5. D

III.1. C 2. C 3. B 4. A 5. C

Level 3 Test 35

I. 1. shrunk 2. postponed 3. marvelous 4. deed 5. lively

II. 1. A 2. B 3. D 4. E 5. C

III.1. D 2. A 3. B 4. D 5. C

Level 3 Test 36

I. 1. sighed 2. lobby 3. shallow 4. pity 5. colony

II. 1. D 2. B 3. C 4. A 5. E

III.1. B 2. A 3. A 4. B 5. C

Level 3 Test 37

I. 1. transport 2. historic 3. spoil 4. bleed 5. dessert

II. 1. C 2. A 3. E 4. B 5. D

III.1. B 2. D 3. B 4. A 5. C

Level 3 Test 38

I. 1. elements 2. poured 3. producer 4. ivory 5. headlines

II. 1. D 2. B 3. A 4. C 5. E

III.1. B 2. C 3. A 4. C 5. C

Level 3 Test 39

I. 1. slaves 2. pretended 3. continent 4. ambassador 5. wrists

II. 1. D 2. E 3. C 4. A 5. B

III.1. B 2. A 3. A 4. D 5. C

Level 3 Test 40

I. 1. tutor 2. slippery 3. ambulance 4. heap 5. energetic

II. 1. E 2. A 3. D 4. B 5. C

III.1. A 2. D 3. A 4. D 5. B

Level 4 Test 1

I. 1. sympathy 2. launched 3. initial 4. endure 5. confidence

II. 1. D 2. C 3. E 4. A 5. B

III.1. B 2. A 3. C 4. D 5. C

Level 4 Test 2

I. 1. intense 2. blends 3. resistance 4. equality 5. continuous

II. 1. C 2. E 3. A 4. D 5. B

III.1. D 2. A 3. C 4. C 5. B

Level 4 Test 3

I. 1. universal 2. measures 3. fastened 4. appropriate 5. incident

II. 1. D 2. B 3. C 4. A 5. E

III.1. C 2. A 3. B 4. A 5. C

Level 4 Test 4

I. 1. constructive 2. reflected 3. guilty 4. behavior 5. vessels

II. 1. C 2. D 3. E 4. B 5. A

III.1. C 2. A 3. B 4. C 5. A

Level 4 Test 5

I. 1. observation 2. cruelty 3. breed 4. reforms 5. eventual

II. 1. B 2. A 3. D 4. E 5. C

III.1. B 2. C 3. D 4. B 5. A

Level 4 Test 6

I. 1. knob 2. moderate 3. curiosity 4. definite 5. rebel

II. 1. E 2. B 3. C 4. A 5. D

III.1. C 2. B 3. A 4. D 5. C

Level 4 Test 7

I. 1. multiple 2. surgery 3. charity 4. messenger 5. phenomenon

II. 1. D 2. B 3. A 4. C 5. E

III.1. B 2. A 3. B 4. C 5. D

Level 4 Test 8

I. 1. nevertheless 2. recovery 3. urgent 4. collapse 5. contrast

II. 1. E 2. B 3. A 4. D 5. C

III.1. A 2. C 3. B 4. A 5. A

Level 4 Test 9
I. 1. Minister 2. abandon 3. reservations
4. harsh 5. refusal
II. 1. D 2. C 3. A 4. B 5. E
III.1. C 2. D 3. A 4. B 5. B

Level 4 Test 10
I. 1. prompted 2. hesitation 3. ingredients
4. involved 5. competitive
II. 1. A 2. D 3. B 4. C 5. E
III.1. C 2. B 3. D 4. C 5. A

Level 4 Test 11
I. 1. neglecting 2. monument 3. accent
4. renew 5. pursue
II. 1. E 2. D 3. B 4. C 5. A
III.1. B 2. A 3. A 4. B 5. A

Level 4 Test 12
I. 1. reputation 2. revise 3. infection
4. labor 5. instinct
II. 1. D 2. E 3. C 4. B 5. A
III.1. A 2. C 3. D 4. B 5. C

Level 4 Test 13
I. 1. disguise 2. emphasis 3. otherwise
4. ruins 5. resembles
II. 1. B 2. C 3. E 4. A 5. D
III.1. B 2. C 3. A 4. B 5. D

Level 4 Test 14
I. 1. instructor 2. engineering 3. authority
4. overthrow 5. outstanding
II. 1. D 2. E 3. B 4. C 5. A
III.1. B 2. C 3. B 4. A 5. C

Level 4 Test 15
I. 1. privileges 2. rewarded 3. fort
4. district 5. carved
II. 1. E 2. C 3. D 4. A 5. B
III.1. D 2. A 3. D 4. B 5. A

Level 4 Test 16
I. 1. manual 2. bond 3. functional
4. publication 5. campaign
II. 1. B 2. D 3. A 4. E 5. C
III.1. C 2. D 3. A 4. B 5. D

Level 4 Test 17
I. 1. signature 2. site 3. precise
4. combination 5. slight
II. 1. C 2. E 3. A 4. B 5. D
III.1. B 2. B 3. B 4. D 5. C

Level 4 Test 18
I. 1. software 2. generosity 3. scarcely
4. comment 5. possessing
II. 1. B 2. E 3. D 4. C 5. A
III.1. B 2. C 3. C 4. D 5. B

Level 4 Test 19
I. 1. secure 2. contents 3. procedure
4. elsewhere 5. feedback
II. 1. D 2. C 3. E 4. B 5. A
III.1. A 2. D 3. B 4. B 5. A

Level 4 Test 20
I. 1. identify 2. associated 3. foundation
4. encounter 5. remedy
II. 1. B 2. D 3. A 4. C 5. E
III.1. B 2. C 3. A 4. B 5. A

Level 4 Test 21
I. 1. embassy 2. globe 3. emerges
4. prosperous 5. singular
II. 1. B 2. C 3. D 4. E 5. A
III.1. D 2. B 3. D 4. B 5. D

Level 4 Test 22
I. 1. civilians 2. imitations 3. partnership
4. enclosed 5. misunderstanding
II. 1. E 2. A 3. B 4. C 5. D
III.1. A 2. C 3. D 4. B 5. A

Level 4 Test 23
I. 1. negotiate 2. lectures 3. immigrated
4. violation 5. endanger
II. 1. A 2. B 3. E 4. C 5. D
III.1. D 2. C 3. A 4. B 5. B

Level 4 Test 24
I. 1. demonstration 2. enforce 3. lipstick
4. burglar 5. frown
II. 1. A 2. E 3. C 4. B 5. D
III.1. B 2. C 3. B 4. B 5. A

Level 4 Test 25

I. 1. committed 2. lengthen 3. nuclear
4. reflection 5. welfare

II. 1. B 2. C 3. A 4. E 5. D

III.1. B 2. D 3. D 4. B 5. A

Level 4 Test 26

I. 1. recreation 2. registered 3. impression
4. loans 5. companion

II. 1. B 2. E 3. D 4. C 5. A

III.1. B 2. C 3. A 4. B 5. D

Level 4 Test 27

I. 1. injured 2. noble 3. accountant
4. shady 5. greasy

II. 1. D 2. E 3. B 4. C 5. A

III.1. D 2. B 3. D 4. A 5. A

Level 4 Test 28

I. 1. suggestion 2. inspection 3. nonsense
4. orbit 5. tomb

II. 1. E 2. B 3. D 4. C 5. A

III.1. B 2. D 3. D 4. B 5. A

Level 4 Test 29

I. 1. rejection 2. blessing 3. acquaintance
4. fantasy 5. sway

II. 1. D 2. A 3. B 4. E 5. C

III.1. C 2. C 3. A 4. B 5. D

Level 4 Test 30

I. 1. awaiting 2. cottage 3. blinking
4. panel 5. giggling

II. 1. B 2. A 3. E 4. C 5. D

III.1. A 2. C 3. A 4. B 5. A

Level 4 Test 31

I. 1. slogan 2. coward 3. bald
4. troublesome 5. intermediate

II. 1. C 2. A 3. B 4. E 5. D

III.1. B 2. C 3. A 4. B 5. D

Level 4 Test 32

I. 1. memorize 2. loyalty 3. telescope
4. ballet 5. feasting

II. 1. D 2. A 3. E 4. B 5. C

III.1. B 2. C 3. A 4. B 5. A

Level 4 Test 33

I. 1. bandage 2. conversed 3. disgusted
4. luxury 5. obstacles

II. 1. E 2. A 3. B 4. C 5. D

III.1. D 2. D 3. C 4. B 5. A

Level 4 Test 34

I. 1. amuse 2. resolved 3. illustrations
4. thoughtful 5. corresponding

II. 1. D 2. B 3. A 4. E 5. C

III.1. B 2. C 3. A 4. D 5. A

Level 4 Test 35

I. 1. costume 2. crush 3. fortunate
4. annoyed 5. statistics

II. 1. C 2. E 3. A 4. B 5. D

III.1. A 2. B 3. D 4. C 5. C

Level 4 Test 36

I. 1. drift 2. cubes 3. greetings
4. postage 5. reunion

II. 1. D 2. A 3. E 4. B 5. C

III.1. D 2. C 3. C 4. B 5. B

Level 4 Test 37

I. 1. idle 2. flea 3. ceases 4. frustration
5. sacrifice

II. 1. E 2. A 3. B 4. C 5. D

III.1. D 2. A 3. A 4. B 5. C

Level 4 Test 38

I. 1. summarize 2. seize 3. arches
4. flushing 5. complicated

II. 1. C 2. A 3. D 4. E 5. B

III.1. D 2. D 3. A 4. B 5. B

Level 4 Test 39

I. 1. curls 2. motivated 3. innocence
4. rhyme 5. proceeding

II. 1. B 2. D 3. A 4. E 5. C

III.1. C 2. B 3. B 4. D 5. B

Level 4 Test 40

I. 1. forbidden 2. yawning 3. parachuting
4. misfortune 5. confessed

II. 1. E 2. A 3. D 4. B 5. C

III.1. B 2. A 3. A 4. B 5. A

Level 5–1 Test 1
I. 1. boost 2. drought 3. equivalent 4. pension 5. overtake
II. 1. D 2. C 3. E 4. B 5. A
III. 1. C 2. A 3. D 4. B 5. C

Level 5–1 Test 2
I. 1. yielded 2. worship 3. personnel 4. chaos 5. interference
II. 1. A 2. B 3. E 4. D 5. C
III. 1. C 2. B 3. C 4. B 5. A

Level 5–1 Test 3
I. 1. celebrity 2. kidnapping 3. elaborate 4. colonial 5. adolescent
II. 1. B 2. D 3. C 4. E 5. A
III. 1. B 2. D 3. A 4. A 5. C

Level 5–1 Test 4
I. 1. interior 2. conceal 3. soaked 4. participants 5. advocate
II. 1. B 2. D 3. A 4. E 5. C
III. 1. D 2. B 3. D 4. C 5. A

Level 5–1 Test 5
I. 1. converted 2. mammal 3. exaggeration 4. reared 5. indifferent
II. 1. C 2. B 3. E 4. D 5. A
III. 1. A 2. B 3. A 4. D 5. B

Level 5–1 Test 6
I. 1. peasants 2. epidemic 3. immune 4. manipulated 5. alternate
II. 1. E 2. D 3. B 4. C 5. A
III. 1. C 2. B 3. B 4. A 5. D

Level 5–1 Test 7
I. 1. complexities 2. specialist 3. perceived 4. fatigue 5. substitute
II. 1. D 2. C 3. E 4. A 5. B
III. 1. A 2. A 3. D 4. B 5. B

Level 5–1 Test 8
I. 1. commissioned 2. lest 3. undermine 4. preference 5. accommodations
II. 1. C 2. D 3. E 4. B 5. A
III. 1. D 2. C 3. B 4. D 5. A

Level 5–1 Test 9
I. 1. appliances 2. manifested 3. explicit 4. decent 5. specimens
II. 1. B 2. E 3. A 4. C 5. D
III. 1. B 2. A 3. B 4. D 5. A

Level 5–1 Test 10
I. 1. extinction 2. massively 3. highlights 4. terminal 5. modified
II. 1. C 2. E 3. A 4. B 5. D
III. 1. B 2. A 3. D 4. C 5. C

Level 5–1 Test 11
I. 1. tribute 2. stocks 3. acquainted 4. extension 5. mounting
II. 1. D 2. A 3. C 4. B 5. E
III. 1. C 2. A 3. A 4. B 5. C

Level 5–1 Test 12
I. 1. pledge 2. antique 3. assessed 4. random 5. strained
II. 1. C 2. A 3. D 4. B 5. E
III. 1. D 2. D 3. A 4. C 5. B

Level 5–1 Test 13
I. 1. legitimate 2. plunge 3. glared 4. derived 5. compatible
II. 1. C 2. B 3. A 4. E 5. D
III. 1. B 2. A 3. B 4. D 5. C

Level 5–1 Test 14
I. 1. sturdy 2. superstition 3. beware 4. vicious 5. caution
II. 1. C 2. D 3. A 4. B 5. E
III. 1. D 2. B 3. C 4. A 5. C

Level 5–1 Test 15
I. 1. precautions 2. subsequent 3. compounds 4. discriminate 5. nowhere
II. 1. D 2. A 3. C 4. B 5. E
III. 1. C 2. A 3. A 4. C 5. B

Level 5–1 Test 16
I. 1. habitats 2. prejudice 3. opponent 4. comprehension 5. blast
II. 1. A 2. C 3. B 4. E 5. D
III. 1. D 2. D 3. A 4. B 5. A

Level 5-1 Test 17

I. 1. conducts 2. prospect 3. initiated
4. institute 5. sandals

II. 1. B 2. D 3. A 4. C 5. E

III. 1. C 2. A 3. C 4. D 5. B

Level 5-1 Test 18

I. 1. dissolved 2. organisms 3. housing
4. bullied 5. whereas

II. 1. B 2. D 3. A 4. E 5. C

III. 1. C 2. A 3. A 4. B 5. A

Level 5-1 Test 19

I. 1. output 2. document 3. sentiment
4. partly 5. agony

II. 1. B 2. D 3. A 4. C 5. E

III. 1. A 2. A 3. D 4. D 5. C

Level 5-1 Test 20

I. 1. virtual 2. decline 3. patrol
4. impulse 5. embrace

II. 1. A 2. B 3. D 4. C 5. E

III. 1. C 2. A 3. B 4. B 5. A